D0259401

SCOTTISH FISHING BOATS

by
Gloria Wilson

HUTTON PRESS
1995

Published by

The Hutton Press Ltd.,
130 Canada Drive,
Cherry Burton, Beverley,
North Humberside HU17 7SB

Copyright © 1995

No part of this book may be reproduced, stored in a
retrieval system, or transmitted in any form or by any
means electronic, mechanical, photocopying, recording
or otherwise, without the prior permission of the
Publisher and the Copyright holders.

Printed and bound by

Clifford Ward & Co. (Bridlington) Ltd.
55 West Street, Bridlington,
East Yorkshire YO15 3DZ

ISBN 1 872167 66 7

CONTENTS

Page

PREFACE

Scottish fishermen are regarded as some of the world's most skilful and technically advanced and their boats are known for their superb standards of seaworthiness.

The last twenty-five years in particular have seen tremendous developments in the design of vessels and their equipment. In 1969 the 78ft wooden hulled cruiser sterned seiner-trawler *Forthright* KY173 was looked upon as being one of the most stalwart and well equipped boats of her size and type.

With beam of 22ft and depth of 12ft 3in she was powered by a 400 hp engine, and for net handling she carried a winch and power block.

In her wheelhouse were half-a-dozen electronic instruments for fishfinding, navigation and communication. She was constructed in the traditional wooden boat-building manner with planking fastened onto oak frames.

Compare her shape with that of *Westro* INS20, built twenty-three years later. At only 75ft long overall this rugged and capacious fully shelter-decked transom sterned steel trawler is 3ft beamier than *Forthright* and 2ft deeper. She was designed and fitted out in Scotland but the plates and sections were cut and shaped in Holland and her hull constructed in England.

And look at the lavishy equipped 92ft steel seiner-trawler *Auriga III* LH449 built in 1989. Having massive beam of near on 27ft she is powered by a 900 hp engine and carries more than twenty-five electronic instruments including one which displays on a screen in the wheelhouse the shape and performance of the net in the water.

Her trawl winches are controlled by computer and she is equipped with a dozen separate items of hydraulically driven gear handling machinery.

Two gutting machines help to reduce manual work for the crew-members and her fishroom is fitted with a chilling plant.

Refinements such as side thrusters, a bulbous bow and steering nozzle with flap rudder enhance her handling qualities. Accommodation for her crew includes a lounge with TV set, and her skipper's quarters include a bathroom and desk.

Nevertheless she is only a couple of feet longer than, say, the 90ft wooden hulled steam drifter *Norlan* BCK177 built in 1914. There may seem little connection between *Norlan* and *Auriga III* but a continuous thread, a gradual shift of ideas and influences can be traced from one to the other, reflecting the changing needs of the fishermen, the advances in technology and the altering circumstances within the fishing industry.

This book sets out to tell something of the story of Scottish fishing vessel design from the mid nineteenth century to the start of the 1990s but does not claim to be comprehensive.

The writer has chosen to concentrate largely on boats within the 40ft to 80ft Registered Length size range, built since the 1950s and belonging to the east coast of mainland Scotland because these are the boats she knows the best.

With only a handful of exceptions she has visited the vessels described and has been to sea with some of them.

And as a general type, the Scottish seiner trawler has an excellent reputation in terms of efficiency and success, adaptability and handiness and seakeeping characteristics.

There is no such thing as a standard Scottish fishing boat. The writer has been fascinated by the way in which almost every boat has a unique personality and character. Fishermen regard the boats as individuals and discuss their merits and peculiarities in critical detail. It is this strong individual spirit which makes the Scottish fishing fleet so alive and colourful and rich in diversity and quality.

But the book is not just a happy documentation of continuous evolution and growing efficiency and prosperity.

There have been nasty economic recessions when fishermen and boat builders thought their industries were doomed.

And the fishing industry is moving into the 1990s against a political and economic background of ever-increasing complexity. These and other issues are touched upon in an attempt to place the boats within their setting.

The writer has written the book in the hope that it will be of interest to those who wish to know more about the Scottish fishing boat and her evolution.

ACKNOWLEDGEMENTS

I am grateful to the numerous people who have given me the information which is used in this book.

Although it is courtesy to mention individuals by name this would be a difficult task as they must surely amount to several hundred! The book is a distillation of a long involvement with the Scottish fishing fleet and boatbuilding yards.

So my thanks are extended to the very many people to whom I have spoken on quaysides and piers and slipways, and in boatyards, offices, factories and fishmarkets all round the coast of Scotland and in many parts of England, and to those who have answered my letters.

My particular thanks go to the skippers and crew members who made me welcome on board their boats. I have happy memories of trips to sea with some of them.

Much of the material covering the years 1971 to 1981 was collected when I was with the weekly journal *Fishing News* and a number of my photographs first published in that paper are used here.

Fisheries statistics are based on the Department of Agriculture and Fisheries for Scotland *Scottish Sea Fisheries Statistical Tables* published by HMSO.

Chapter 1
HISTORY AND DEVELOPMENT — EARLY BOATS

The modern Scottish fishing boat has evolved through many changes from small open double-ended clinker built rowing and sailing craft of Norse origin which were used by crofter fishermen living in scattered communities prior to the nineteenth century.

A vigorous herring fishery developed during the nineteenth century. As a result of the Industrial Revolution, large towns were growing, thus providing extensive markets for fish. The opening of railways meant that fish could be transported quickly to these large centres of population.

New markets for Scottish cured herring were also opened up in Germany, Poland and Russia.

Three main types of sailing boat were built.

Scaffie.

The scaffie was favoured on the Moray Firth. Clinker planked and double-ended she was full at the stern with steeply raked sternpost, curved stem and flat somewhat hollow floors and low bilges.

Owing to her short keel she answered readily to the helm and the cutaway forefoot kept damage to the minimum if she was driven over her own drift nets.

However, the raked stern and fullness aft made the scaffie dangerous in a following sea and the rounded bow did not grip the water well and could turn her away from the wind.

A typical decked scaffie was 60ft long with 36ft keel and beam of 17ft 5in. Her tall dipping lug sail had a broad foot which helped to keep her head to the wind and compensated for the lack of keel length. A standing lug was carried on the mizzen mast.

Fifies.

The latter half of the nineteenth century saw the full development of the famous decked east coast fifie, characterised by the almost vertical stem and sternpost, deep heel and forefoot, long straight keel and steep slightly hollow floors.

Her upright stern made the fifie safer than the scaffie when running before the seas and the deep forefoot afforded a better grip in the water and helped her to point well up into the wind, but she manoeuvred less easily because of the long keel.

She was rigged with a huge high-peaked dipping lug sail and a standing lug mizzen.

Both the scaffie and fifie sometimes set a jib when making a passage in fine weather.

Typically a larger carvel planked fifie measured 72ft long with a beam of 20ft 6in and her foremast rose 55ft from the deck. Able to carry three hundred crans of herring she had a crew of eight and worked seventy drift nets.

Zulus.

In 1879 the first zulu was built, combining the advantages of the fifie with those of the scaffie.

With vertical stem and raked sternpost she had the handiness of the scaffie and the seakeeping qualities and weatherly capabilities of the fifie.

In general, fifies were owned along the east coast from Fraserburgh to Eyemouth while the zulu superseded the scaffie in Moray Firth ports.

Hundreds of fifies and zulus up to some 80ft long took part in the English and Scottish herring fishings.

Zulus were so popular that 480 were registered at Buckie alone in 1900.

One small zulu the 45ft *Violet* FR451 fished from Fraserburgh for more than sixty years. Built by Wilson Noble and Co. at Fraserburgh in 1911 she was later fitted with motor and wheelhouse.

Steam.

Towards the close of the nineteenth century steam powered fishing boats were introduced to Scotland. Some of the earliest were built on the Firth of Forth for great-line

Sailing fifies leaving for the herring grounds in 1901.
Photograph courtesy
James N. Miller and Sons Ltd.

*The zulu **Nimrod** BF1028 setting out from Peterhead with her crew raising the huge dipping lug sail. Note the rake of her sternpost.*
Photograph courtesy
North East of Scotland
Museums Service.

Built by Herd and Mackenzie at Findochty in 1910 **Sterlochy** BCK65 was a typical wooden hulled steam, drifter. 'Herdies' was founded in 1903 and built some forty steam drifters ending with the 90ft **Lizzie West** in 1930.
Photograph courtesy Moray District Council.

The 90ft wooden hulled steam drifter **Norlan** BCK177 was built in Buckie by Thomson and Stewart in 1914.

9

fishing. Steam trawling was adopted in Aberdeen in the 1880s.

Around 1900 the larger sailing drifters began to give way to counter sterned steam vessels which were independent of wind conditions and could make longer trips to find herring which were now further away from land.

Many early steam drifters were built in England but by 1910 Scottish yards were producing them in large numbers, based on the style of the English vessels.

Normally wooden hulled steam drifters were 75ft to 90ft long with an elliptical counter stern, vertical stem and little sheer. They were less beamy than the sailing boats but had deeper bulwarks, and were powered by triple expansion engines and had a steam driven capstan for hauling nets.

Surmounted by a tall funnel the superstructure was aft and contained wheelhouse, engine-room casing and galley. A small mizzen sail kept the drifter's head to the wind when fishing. Many steam drifters were built of steel, in English and Scottish yards.

Steam engines with their boilers and coal bunkers were too big and heavy for use on smaller vessels and also needed a fireman. A cheaper source of power the internal combustion engine, which could be fitted into existing sailing craft, was introduced around the turn of the century and quickly found favour.

One of the first large fifies to be successfully converted was the 66ft *Maggie Jane's* BK146 from Eyemouth. She was fitted with a 55hp Gardner paraffin engine in 1907.

Fifies made suitable conversions as the vertical sternpost was not weakened by the propeller aperture.

By 1909 there were thirty-five motor boats on the Scottish east coast.

Out of a total of 8,124 fishing vessels registered in Scotland in 1919, 324 were steam trawlers, 872 steam drifters, 1,844 motor boats and 5,084 sailing craft.

Important changes.

Important changes took place in the Scottish fishing industry in the 1920s and '30s mainly resulting from the effects of war and recession, and the development of new catching techniques.

Steam drifters became uneconomical to run and many were laid up, because of diminishing catches and poor prices, the coal dispute in 1921, and the loss of eastern European herring markets brought about by political changes.

Many fishermen began to look to other forms of fishing.

Seining.

Around 1918 several Danish motor boats which caught white fish using the seine net landed catches at English ports.

English fishermen took rapidly to this method of fishing, and in 1920 a number of Scottish steam drifters bought seine net gear in Grimsby and steamed home to fish for haddock, cod, plaice and lemon sole in the Moray Firth.

The Scots developed seine netting into the technique known as 'fly-dragging' which was ideal for working on the mixture of rough and smooth ground off the Scottish coast and was effective in catching more of the faster and higher swimming cod, haddock and whiting in addition to flatfish.

From the mid 1920s steam drifters declined in numbers and very few were built. Instead, a fleet of medium sized fifie-type motor boats for use in line, shellfish, herring fishing and especially seining, began to build up. They had less draught than the sailing craft with flatter floors and rounded forefoot.

The first boat specifically constructed for seine netting in Scotland was the 50ft motor fifie *Marigold* INS234 built at Lossiemouth in 1927 for Skipper John Campbell.

Seine netters, ring netters, and the cruiser and canoe stern.

Towards the close of the 1920s the cruiser stern was adopted in Scotland.

J. and G. Forbes and Co. at Sandhaven had built cruiser sterned fishing boats for England some years previously, including two 55 footers for Grimsby owners in 1916.

Olive BF123 *was a characterstic motor fifie. Built by W. G. Stephen at Macduff in 1929 she was 39.9ft long with 12.9ft beam. Her sternpost had a slight rake.*

Scottish motor fifies became well-liked in England. W. G. Stephen of Macduff built the 43ft **Galilee** *WY68 for Whitby in 1932. On one occasion she was hauling crab and lobster pots but the catch was poor. A box floated past with 'Keep Smiling' written on it.*

*Early Moray Firth seine netter **Fruition** INS265 in Lossiemouth. Measuring 50ft by 15ft she was built at Banff in 1933. Note her cruiser stern and narrow gutted hull form.*

*The 75ft cruiser sterned motor drifter **Gleanaway** KY40 in Yarmouth. Built in 1930 for Provost William Carstairs of Cellardyke she had a 140hp Fairbanks Morse diesel engine and a steam capstan.*
Photograph courtesy
The Scottish Fisheries Museum Trust Ltd.

Cairntoul PD394 was built as **Poppy** BCK41 in 1934.
She was an early large cruiser sterned motor boat. Note her lean and narrow-gutted lines.

Forbes produced the 45ft cruiser sterned *Cutty Sark* FR334 in 1928 as a multi-purpose boat able to switch to seining, lining and herring fishing. She was broadly based on the Danish type of cruiser sterned seiner, but her stem was vertical rather than rounded.

Throughout the 1930s Scottish yards built dozens of wooden-hulled cruiser sterned diesel-engined seine net vessels in the 50ft to 60ft size range. Normally the wheelhouse was aft and winch and rope coiler forward. Multi cylinder diesel engines were relatively light weight compared with earlier semi-diesels and were also easier on fuel than paraffin engines. The round form of the cruiser stern afforded more manoeuvrability and the rudder was tucked underneath leaving the stern obstruction-free for working the seine net. By now, herring prices had improved and large cruiser sterned motor boats were built as economical successors to the steam drifter, and designed to work as seiners or liners between the herring seasons.

One such vessel was the 75ft x 18.75ft *Gleanaway* KY 40 built by Forbes in 1930 and powered by a four-cylinder two-stroke cycle 140hp diesel engine. She fished with seventy-two drift nets which extended for one and a half miles.

Another was the 77ft *Poppy* BCK 41 built by Thomson and Stewart at Buckie in 1934 with a National 120hp diesel engine.

Gleanaway and *Poppy* were among sixteen motor boats which went to the East Anglian herring fishing in 1935.

Pleased.

These vessels pleased the fishermen with their sea-keeping qualities and general comfort and their low running costs. *Gleanaway* did ten knots and was claimed

13

*An attractive example of a pre-war cruiser sterned dual purpose motor boat, the 69ft **Dundarg** FR121 was built by Wilson Noble and Co. at Fraserburgh in 1939. She had a beam of 19ft and cost £3,000 to build.*

Built in 1921 the ring netter **Falcon** *CN97 marked the introduction of the canoe stern.* Photograph courtesy James N. Miller and Sons Ltd.

to be the 'fastest boat in existence'. During 4½ weeks at the west coast herring fishing in 1931 she earned £350 which gave her crew £21.16s each. A steamer grossed £330 during the same period, but higher expenses left her crew with only £12.9s apiece.

Smaller canoe sterned boats of light build and shallow draught were built for herring ring netting in relatively sheltered waters, particularly off the Scottish west coast. The first was the 50ft *Falcon* CN97 built by James N. Miller and Sons at St. Monans in 1921 for Robert Robertson of Campbeltown.

Introduced to the west of Scotland during the nineteenth century ring netting became more generally accepted after World War I.

Ring net vessels needed to be very manoeuvrable and were much admired for their sweet and elegant lines.

East coast fishermen particularly in Firth of Forth ports also owned canoe sterned ring netters. There was a vigorous winter herring fishery off the Fife coast.

In 1938 the total Scottish fishing fleet comprised 5,067 vessels. There were 320 steam trawlers, 26 steam liners, 402 steam drifters, 2,471 motor boats and 1,848 sailing craft. The sailing boats were in the main very small.

After World War II.

In the early post-war years, and up until the start of the 1960s, the basic design of the cruiser sterned diesel-engined wooden boat was little changed, but with a general move towards more powerful fuller-bodied vessels with greater sea range and catching capacities and fitted with electronic navigation and fish-finding instruments.

Financial assistance from the White Fish Authority and the Herring Industry Board helped fishermen to buy new boats.

Seine net fishing gained in importance and by the early 1960s was the chief means of catching white fish in Scotland.

Seine netters were usually some 40ft to 70ft long with beam of 15ft to 20ft and were stoutly built to withstand

Morayshire INS212 putting to sea from Lossiemouth in the 1970s. Her builders Herd and Mackenzie who had moved to Buckie constructed its first cruiser sterned boat in 1933. Built in 1948 **Morayshire** *was beamier than the yard's pre-war seiners.*

severe conditions in the North Sea and off the north west coast of Scotland. An early post war example was the 62ft x 18ft *Morayshire* INS212 built by Herd and Mackenzie at Buckie in 1948 and powered by a Gardner 114hp diesel engine.

*The 63ft seiner **Rowan Tree** INS290 was built by James Noble (Fraserburgh) Ltd. in 1955. With a beam of 18ft she was powered by a Gardner 152hp diesel engine. Note the coils of seine rope on her deck.*
Photograph author's collection.

Guiding Star *PD322 in Eyemouth.*
Built in 1959 she was 51ft long with beam of 16ft 6in.
*Compare her fuller beamier form with that of **Fruition**.*

In 1957 the same builder launched the slightly larger *Mayflower* INS35 for Lossiemouth owners. Measuring 65ft x 19ft she was equipped with a Gardner 152hp engine, Sutherland winch and Beccles rope coiler, Coastal radiotelephone, Kelvin Hughes echosounder and Decca Navigator, all these being usual fittings in many seiners at that time.

D. F. Sutherland of Lossiemouth had made hundreds of mechanically-driven seine net winches, the majority powered from the main engine through a shaft running forward beneath the fishroom floor. The Beccles coiler, chain driven from the winch, was made by Elliott and Garrood of Beccles in Suffolk.

Decca Navigator.

Invented in 1939 the Decca Navigator was a reliable position finding instrument which picked up radio signals transmitted from shore-based stations. The indicator unit in the wheelhouse gave readings which, when transferred to a marine chart overprinted with a network of numbered position lines or 'lanes', gave the boat's position.

The echosounder operated on the principle of sound waves which were generated electrically and transmitted downwards from a transducer on the vessel's hull. Echoes were returned to the transducer when the impulses passed through any medium other than water.

An echosounder could indicate the distance of the target from the boat's keel by measuring the time lapse between the transmitted signal and the reception of its echo. Thus the depth and contour of the seabed and the presence of shoals of fish could be registered as marks on paper in the recording unit in the wheelhouse.

Some more from the 1950s.

Smaller seiners included *Guiding Star* PD322 built in 1959 by the Macduff Engineering Co. Measuring 51ft x 16ft 6in she was powered by a Gardner 114hp diesel engine. Her wheelhouse was wooden and she carried winch and coiler, echosounder, radio and Decca Navigator. She was typical of many seiners built by Macduff around that time.

Dual purpose craft up to 75ft or so were built for herring drifting and great lining in addition to seine net fishing.

Some beauties came from the Fraserburgh area where four yards were active in the 1950s.

One of the most well known boats was *Fertile* FR305 built by J. and G. Forbes in 1954 for Peterhead, but later owned in Fraserburgh by the Tait family of skilful herring fishermen.

She was 75ft long with beam of 20ft and powered by a National 200hp engine.

Further south, Smith and Hutton (Boatbuilders) Ltd. of Anstruther built the 75ft x 20ft *Silver Chord* KY124 in 1957 for Skipper James Muir.

She replaced the port's last steam drifter *Coriedalis* KY21 and in 1957 won the Prunier Trophy for the biggest single catch of herring during the East Anglian season. Later she concentrated on great line fishing.

Scottish cruiser sterned wooden craft were wonderful seaboats. *Silver Chord* for example proved her seakeeping abilities when off Faroe in atrocious conditions. A sea rolled her onto her starboard beam, and her wheelhouse touched the water, but she righted herself again. She also worked lines at Rockall, two-hundred miles west of the Outer Hebrides and known as the place where bad weather was invented.

Attractive.

Smith and Hutton also produced seiners and dual purpose boats in the 40ft to 55ft size range. *Success* KY211 was built for Whitby in 1960. Her skipper, Jim Leadley, was one of the first on the Yorkshire coast to work Scottish seine netting.

She had attractive lines and was 55ft long with beam of 17ft and extreme depth of 10ft. Skipper Leadley said 'She takes some punishment. She's good at running before a heavy following sea because she isn't too full aft'.

Fertile FR305 was one of Scotland's most successful herring drifters. She is seen here coming into Fraserburgh after a herring fishing trip. Note the drift nets on deck.

Silver Chord KY124 made great-lining trips lasting a fortnight to three weeks. Using squid or herring as bait she caught large fish such as halibut, ling and skate. Early in her career she worked herring drift nets and won the Prunier Trophy at Yarmouth in 1957.

Success KY211 in Whitby. Note her seine winch and rope coiler abaft the foremast. She had sweet lines.

A lull.

During the early 1960s there was a lull in fishing boat building in Scotland. The White Fish Authority felt that the fleet had reached sufficient strength and reduced its Grant and Loan scheme which had been in operation since 1953 to help fishermen buy new vessels.

A restricted scheme offered assistance for replacements to old decrepit craft. In 1963 Smith and Hutton built the 55ft seiner *Altair* LH418 to replace the elderly Eyemouth boat *Victory* INS37. *Altair* had the new Gardner 6L3B engine rated at 150hp at 1,000 rpm.

The 1960s.

A great many changes.

In the early 1960s a great many things began to happen. They brought about the building of a new generation of boats which featured innovations in virtually every aspect of their design, construction and equipment.

Broadly speaking the changes were effected by new fishing methods and advances in technology, and a general growth in the home-water fisheries following the extension of Britain's territorial waters from three to twelve miles in 1964.

Pair trawling and purse seining.

During the 1950s it became evident that the herring shoals were not following their normal pattern of movement. Herring became scanty in the North Sea where in previous years drifters had made big hauls.

Landings at Peterhead alone, for many years a chief herring port, fell from 108,090 crans in 1952 to 6,810 in 1964 and a similar pattern was forming off the English coast.

Although the drifters were having a lean time, Continental boats using herring trawls and purse seines continued to make plentiful hauls and the Scots realised

20

that they must look for alternative methods to drifting in order to increase their catching power. Trawling for herring had been done fifty years previously by British fishermen and in the 1950s a few Irish and Scottish boats had worked the light Danish midwater trawl.

In the late 1950s and early 1960s the Herring Industry Board sent parties of herring fishermen to study the midwater trawling techniques used by the Dutch, Danes and Swedes.

The Scots were so impressed that several began to equip their boats for the fishing. Among the first were Fraserburgh skippers George Watt and William Cowe with the 61ft *Flourish* FR149 and the 55ft *Argosy* FR242. They pair trawled together successfully for herring and sprats in the early 1960s off the east coast from Wick to Bridlington.

The engines and hulls of most existing Scottish drifter/seiners were not powerful enough for single boat trawling for herring, so an advantage of pair trawling was that twice the power was available for towing the one net.

Late in 1965 Skippers Jim Pirie and John Alec Buchan of Peterhead with their new boats *Shemara* PD235 and *Fairweather* PD197 worked the pair trawl off the Scottish west coast and did exceptionally well, and others soon followed suit.

Pair trawlers increased their catching capacity and earning power by developing the 'fleeting' system, working in teams of three or more.

When only two boats worked a pair trawl much of a large shoal could be lost or time wasted when one boat was lying idle while the other brailed the catch aboard.

Should a third vessel be present she could pair up with the idle one and tow through the shoal again. If the group was bigger the herring catching could be even more efficient and a partnership of five could land 2,000 crans within twenty-four hours.

When five or six worked together, two or three could be fishing and the others searching for more shoals or heading for port with full fishrooms to reach an early market.

Huge catches.

Other Scottish skippers were intrigued by the huge catches taken by Norwegian and Icelandic purse seiners and in 1966 Skipper Donald Anderson of Peterhead had his 78ft seiner drifter *Glenugie III* PD347 equipped for this fishing and netted some 11,500 crans in six months.

Pursing and pair trawling began to develop further, and drifters and ringers became fewer and by 1969 the Scottish herring fleet was composed of fifteen purse seiners, forty-three midwater trawlers, fifty-three ring netters and fifteen drifters. In that year trawlers produced some forty per cent of the Scottish herring catch and pursers twelve per cent.

New seine net grounds.

Meanwhile seine net fishing developed enormously during the 1960s. New grounds were exploited further afield and there were big advances in fishing gear technology.

Net makers introduced larger, more efficient nets, and the use of synthetic fibres enabled cod ends to hold much bigger hauls without bursting.

Synthetic materials also began to replace natural fibres for seine net ropes.

There was also a continuing move towards inshore trawling for white fish by boats under 80ft long, which needed to be robust and powerful for working their gear.

Moving towards the 1970s.

The new fishing methods and the further evolution of seining and white fish trawling called for stouter more powerful and sophisticated vessels.

Financial assistance for building new boats was available from the White Fish Authority, the Herring Industry Board and the Highlands and Islands Development Board.

During the 1960s there was a foretaste of the tremendous developments which were to take place later.

In the shape of boats there was an increase in beam and depth in proportion to length with a consequent filling

Cynosure A774 seen here in Aberdeen in the 1970s.
She was one of a series of stout cruiser sterned seiner trawlers
built by James Noble (Fraserburgh) Ltd. during the previous decade.
Note her chunky shape and pronounced sheer. Built in 1967 for Stonehaven owners
she was 50ft long with 17ft 3in beam.

out of hull form. For instance, James Noble (Fraserburgh) Ltd. introduced a new series of sturdy seiner trawlers with fuller lines and strong sheer and more carrying capacity, starting in 1963 with the 55ft *Maureen* WK270. About twenty-five similar craft from 40ft to 60ft long were built by Noble in the subsequent seven or eight years.

The 69ft x 20.2ft *Fairweather* PD197 built by Forbes in 1965 for Skipper John Alec Buchan was a big boat for her size, more substantial in lines and construction than the yard's earlier boats of this length. She was fuller in the bilge and beamier and deeper with extra strength and deck space and carrying capability for working the herring pair trawl.

Her 240hp Kelvin engine was later uprated to 320hp.

For a while she was a member of the Peterhead pair trawling team known as the 'Big Six'.

Overseas.

Financial assistance became available to buy powerful engines of overseas make and in 1964 the 74ft Buckie trawler *Ardelle* BCK227 was fitted with a Mercedes Benz engine of 320 hp and the 79ft Anstruther seiner *Argonaut II* KY357 was equipped with a Caterpillar unit of 325hp.

Designers and manufacturers worked closely with the fishermen to produce equipment which would satisfy the demands of the new and traditional fishing techniques. The WFA's Industrial Development Unit was set up in 1963 to study vessels and machinery and develop improvements and innovations in fishing boat technology.

Hydraulic winches and the power block.

Gear-handling efficiency was vastly improved by the use of hydraulically powered winches and the power block.

In 1966 the IDU held trials with a hydraulic winch drive on the Buckie seiner *Opportune II* BCK60. As opposed to mechanical drive it allowed for infinitely variable control of winch speeds over a wide range of engine speeds and gave independent control of winch and propeller and more flexibility in working the gear.

Although power blocks for net hauling were in use on purse seiners they were not fitted to Scottish fly dragging seiners until the late 1960s.

Under the supervision of the IDU hydraulic power blocks were supplied to the seiners *Argonaut II* and *Ocean Gain* PD438 in 1968.

Hauling the seine net by hand over the stern had been a laborious and dangerous task with crewmen likely to be dragged overboard. Fitted with a rubber coated sheave the power block was mounted on the end of a derrick which could be raised, lowered or slewed. The net was hauled through the block as far as the cod end which was then lifted aboard by use of the gilson derrick.

Use of the block made net hauling much safer and less tiring for the fishermen and enabled gear to be worked in rougher weather, and heavy hauls could be heaved aboard before the cod end touched the seabed and burst.

Power blocks were later adapted for other modes of fishing including herring pair trawling.

By the close of 1969 some forty Scottish seiner trawlers carried the equipment.

More electronics.

Additional electronic instruments coming into widespread use in the 1960s included sonar, fishlupes, radar and the Decca Track Plotter. Herring boats in particular began to use sonar which employed echosounding techniques to detect the presence of fish at a radius around the boat as well as directly underneath.

Normally used as a supplement to the echosounder the fishlupe, or fishscope, displayed echoes on the screen of a cathode ray tube and gave an expanded view of the area above the seabed. The transmitted impulse appeared on the screen as a vertical line and echoes showed as gleaming deflections of the line, the larger the deflection the bigger the shoal of fish.

The Decca Track Plotter was used as an attachment to the Navigator and recorded on a paper chart the course the boat was taking in relation to the Decca lanes. So a record of her movements could be kept, enabling her to return to the same place and repeat successful fishing tows by following the previous track on the chart.

*Built in 1965 by J. and G. Forbes and Co. the 69ft **Fairweather** PD197 was one of the first boats designed and constructed for herring pair trawling. Note her full lines.*

Chapter 2
THE EARLY 1970s; YEARS OF PROSPERITY AND TECHNICAL PROGRESS

Scottish fishermen moved into the 1970s against a background of great technical advances in all sectors of the fishing industry. And demand for fish was increasing on a huge scale giving them earnings looked upon as unattainable several years previously. Almost all species were in very keen demand owing to a growing awareness of the value of fish for human consumption and the general rise in the costs of other protein foods.

The weight and value of all species of fish landed by British vessels at Scottish ports rose from 375,359.8 metric tonnes valued at £22,559,323 in 1969 to 477,209.8 metric tonnes worth £64,061,803 in 1974.

In response to the improving fortunes of the fishermen, boatyards were inundated with orders for wooden and steel vessels with some firms quoting delivery dates several years ahead.

One or two new builders entered the fishing boat market and in all some four hundred new vessels, the majority in the 30ft to 80ft registered length size range, joined the Scottish fleet in the years 1969 to 1974 inclusively.

This enormous investment reflected the confidence of Scottish skippers and vessel owners in the future of their fisheries and their eagerness to have efficient boats able to work the new fishing techniques to advantage.

Things continued happily until 1974 when there was a drop in catches, and the growth in gross earnings began to be overtaken by a savage rise in operating costs largely stemming from the increase in prices of crude oil imposed by the oil producing countries.

Cruiser sterned wooden hulled boats
Forthright and *Steadfast*

Two of my favourite wooden hulled cruiser sterned boats were the 78ft seiner trawlers *Forthright* KY173 and *Steadfast* KY170, built in 1969 by Richard Irvin and Sons Ltd. at Peterhead for Skippers Robert and Alec Gardner of Anstruther in Fife.

Designed by the builders to their skippers' requirements they were sister ships, and differed only in minor details of equipment and appearance. In contrast to the vessels built by Irvin's in the 1950s and early '60s they were hefty beamy boats with deep freeboard and low round bilges and had full lines forward to provide a lot of deckroom around the winch, and space in the fishroom.

When seen alongside *Forthright* and *Steadfast* the earlier boats looked lean and spare and narrow gutted with hardly any definite bilge, and one fisherman said *Forthright* was 'a great lump of a boatie'.

Despite their ample proportions *Forthright* and *Steadfast* had very fair lines. Their floors were very slightly hollow and their stems had quite a pronounced rake, and they were relatively fine lined aft and eyesweet around the stern.

At her skipper's request *Forthright* was given a slightly sharper sheer forward than *Steadfast* to give a more graceful appearance. Their steel deckhouses also differed in shape and *Forthright*'s was fitted further aft.

These and other small variations gave them different characters.

I will describe *Forthright* in some detail because she represented the latest thinking in the design of wooden hulled cruiser sterned boats in the late 1960s.

Overall length was 78ft, beam 22ft, and midships depth from underside of keel to top of deck beam, 12ft 3in.

Below deck she was subdivided from forward into net store, fishroom, engineroom, cabin and steering gear compartment. She was heavily constructed to withstand the rigours of trawling and bear the stress of the powerful engine.

The 2½in and 3½in oak and larch planking was fastened onto double oak frames which were spaced 20in between their centres. The main framework was of oak

Forthright KY173 in Peterhead in the early 1970s.
Note her full forward lines.

and fastened together with 1in diameter bolts, and the deck was planked with oregon pine 2¼in thick.

Deck beams, bulkheads, engine seats, deckhouse, whaleback, main-mast and seine derricks were steel.

Forthright was powered by a Caterpillar D353TA six-cylinder diesel engine which developed 400hp at 1225 rpm to turn a 66in diameter fixed pitch Bruntons propeller through a 4.09:1 reverse and reduction gearbox. The stainless steel tailshaft had a larger than normal diameter of 5in to enable the engine to be uprated to 450hp at a later date if required.

Six-cylinder engines were smoother running than those with fewer cylinders. The reduction gear enabled the boat to have a large diameter slow turning propeller which gave good towing power for trawling. A reduction gear was necessary because modern diesel engines rotated too fast for an efficient propeller. A McLure 110v direct current generator, 24v alternator and Desmi 2in

bilge and general service pump with suction pipes from cabin, engineroom and fishroom were driven from auxiliary power take-offs on the engine.

Another McLure 110v generator, 24v alternator and Desmi pump were powered by a Lister HW3 28.5 hp auxiliary engine. Both engines had electric starting.

Direct current electricity was safer to operate in wooden boats than alternating current systems. The 24v alternators were rectified into direct current for charging the batteries. Steel tanks in the engineroom held some 2,500 gallons of fuel oil and 350 gallons of fresh water, the latter being pumped to the galley by a Stuart Turner pump activated by a switch in the galley.

Aluminium non-slip flooring in the engine room covered moving machinery parts for safety. Natural air vents and the main engine's ventilated exhaust system cooled the engine room.

On deck a 'Mastra' combination seine and trawl winch

made by the Northern Tool and Gear Co. of Arbroath was positioned forward with the trawl drums fitted longitudinally at the fore side of the seine barrels. Each trawl drum held 600 fathoms of 2½in circumference wire warp and the seine barrels were used in conjunction with a Beccles rope coiler chain driven from the winch.

Hydraulic power came from a Dowty variable delivery high pressure pump driven from the extension shaft at the forward end of the main engine. The pump was of the axial piston tilting head type by which oil flow to the fixed delivery Dowty hydraulic motor in the winch could be varied so that hauling speed of the winch was infinitely variable, independently of the engine revolutions.

Pipes forming the closed loop hydraulic circuit between pump and motor were lagged and enclosed in a wooden casing where they passed through the fishroom to prevent heat reaching the catch. Engine and pump controls were sited side by side in the wheelhouse so that any combination of winch and engine speeds could be selected to suit the fishing conditions.

A Dowty fixed delivery pump on the auxiliary engine could be connected to the hydraulic circuit to drive the winch and retrieve the fishing gear in the event of main engine or pump breakdown.

On the after deck a Rapp 19R power block was hung from a crane fitted with lifting and slewing cylinders. Hydraulic power was provided by a Vickers pump driven from the same power-take-off which drove the winch pump.

Controls for block and cylinders were mounted on the slewing post.

Other deck fittings included wooden landing derrick, tungsten iodine floodlights, seine rope leads and Whale hand operated bilge pumps. A gaff mizzen sail helped to keep the boat's head to the wind at sea when required, and seine net gilson derricks for lifting the cod end aboard were mounted on the casing top.

The steel whaleback afforded shelter around the winch. For herring pair-trawling steel gallows with towing blocks were fitted at starboard bow and quarter, a tubular steel gilson derrick was mounted at the starboard side of the mainmast and appropriate sheaves and rollers arranged on deck.

Forthright's fishroom was 30ft long and arranged to carry white fish in boxes or on shelves and herring in bulk. It was divided up with steel stanchions and aluminium pound boards and insulated on both bulkheads with Onazote lined with tongue-and groove redwood and had one steel hatch with aluminium cover. Wooden chutes passed from two bunker rings on deck into the ice lockers. A fish washer on deck utilised water through the deckwash hose of the Desmi pumps.

Wheelhouse.

Instruments in the wheelhouse included Kelvin Hughes type 17 radar which had 8 scale ranges from ¼ to 24 nautical miles, Decca Mk 12 Navigator, S P Sailor radio telephone, Redifon vhf radio telephone, and Elac LAZ17 Echograph Superior recording echosounder type Atair with LAZ61 Fishlupe.

Manufactured in Germany by Electroacustic GMBH, Elac echosounding equipment was supplied by Woodsons of Aberdeen Ltd.

A selection of eight sounding ranges from large scale to a survey of the entire water depth was available on the Echograph whereas the Fishlupe showed the whole depth or expansions of any seven fathoms. In the Fishlupe's expanded mode, echoes were shown separated from one another so that shoal density and the approximate number and size of fish could be estimated. The Fishlupe had steady picture and bottom lock facilities so that echoes remained steady instead of flashing on and off, and the display was not distorted by the boat's movement.

A Kent Clearview revolving screen, which deflected rain and spray, was fitted in a wheelhouse window.

Forthright's Tenfjord H100TC power-assisted hydraulic steering gear enabled her to be steered by wheel or by a small lever in the wheelhouse. An electrically driven hydraulic pump sent oil to the hydraulic motor which turned the rudder.

Hydraulic steering gear was a great advance on the former chain operated equipment and made the rudder move more easily in rough seas.

She pioneered the use in the UK of the Decca 250 automatic pilot. Coupled to the steering gear it enabled her to maintain a pre-selected straight course. If she departed from the course the autopilot automatically took correcting action. Course could also be altered by turning a knob on the autopilot. During trials with the equipment, in heavy weather when pitching and rolling was severe, Skipper Gardner said that it could steer the boat better than a man could.

Forthright's cabin contained seven bunks, electric radiators, gas fire, cupboards and lockers, table and seating. A combined skylight and escape hatch was fitted into the deckhead.

Facilities in the combined galley and messdeck abaft the wheelhouse included gas cooker, stainless steel sink and hot water supply. A lavatory was arranged in the casing.

Forthright had dark blue topsides, white waterline and red underwater body and her deckhouse was painted to resemble wood graining. Wheelhouse and accommodation were lined with wood grain effect plastic laminates.

Steadfast had a Kelvin Hughes automatic pilot and her Fishlupe did not initially have steady picture and bottom lock but otherwise she was similar to *Forthright* in all main particulars.

Successful boats.

I first met *Forthright* and *Steadfast* when they were being built. Occasionally everything disappeared in a

*Forthright KY173 and **Steadfast** KY170 (right) being fitted out.*
Forthright** had a slightly stronger sheer forward than **Steadfast
and their deckhouses differed in shape.

purple fog. This was caused by the welding being done on *Forthright*'s steel beams casting a purplish brilliant light onto clouds of steam. The steam came from the box in which *Steadfast*'s planks were being steamed to make them supple and bendable for fastening to her frames. When their hulls were complete they were launched and fitted out alongside the quay. *Forthright* went down the slipway quickly, making a spectacular splash. Some people attributed her subsequent fishing success to this. She had shown her eagerness to get away to sea by getting out of the shed as rapidly as she could. She was 'raring to be off'.

Apart from making a few herring trawling trips off the Scottish west coast, *Forthright* and *Steadfast* concentrated on flydragging seine net fishing, undertaking trips of less than a week to grounds such as the Bergen Bank some 200 miles north east of Aberdeen.

Catches consisted largely of haddock and cod which were packed in ice in 7-stone wooden boxes, and landings were normally made in Aberdeen but sometimes in Peterhead or North Shields. They were very much 'sister ships' as they often fished in proximity and put ashore their catches on the same day.

During the early 1970s they were among the highest earning Scottish seiners and were known for landing high quality fish nicely presented for auction and in keen demand from the buyers.

Forthright was still fishing from Aberdeen in the early 1990s.

Steadfast sank in 1982 following a collision with an oil rig tender on the Ekofisk oil field. Her crew were picked up by the tender.

The Builders of *Forthright* and *Steadfast*; a brief History

Forthright was the 88th boat to come from her builder's yard, which was founded at Peterhead in 1914. From the early 1950s onwards Irvins became heavily involved in the continuous development of large cruiser sterned boats, mainly for Peterhead owners.

They show a gradual evolution in design from slender vessels 72ft and 73ft long and 19ft 6in on the beam, to the more gutsy and full bodied 78 footers of the late 1960s and early 1970s.

This was a fascinating evolutionary process whereby sometimes only very subtle modifications were made to successive boats, arrived at by careful study of those already fishing and in keeping with each new vessel's equipment and proposed fishing techniques.

Modifications may have been small, but over a period of years they amounted to quite significant changes. In this design and building procedure Irvins was characteristic of many similar yards where a series of vessels was produced within a limited size range.

Fine lined and elegant.

During the 1950s Peterhead was disposing of its steam drifters and Irvins contributed to the port's new fleet of dual-purpose motor boats with about half a dozen fine lined elegant craft designed primarily as drifters or drifter liners. They delighted the fishermen, who considered them ideal replacements to the steam driven vessels.

The 73ft *Silver Hope* PD377 was typical. Built in 1954 she had a Gardner 152hp engine and Sutherland mechanically driven drift net winch. Her lines were very slight in comparison to *Forthright*'s more capacious form. But with the fluctuations in herring fishing, Peterhead fishermen were looking more to the seine net and needed heftier beamier boats.

Accordingly the drifter seiner liner *Starlight* PD149, built for Skipper Alex Baird in 1956, measured 74ft 6in with 20ft beam and was deeper than her predecessors and a bit fuller on the waterline.

Sleek and graceful.

About a dozen more of the *Starlight* type were built, some with minor adjustments to length or lines as thought desirable, but all were sleek and graceful boats much admired for their seakeeping qualities.

Around 1961 fishermen were beginning to work the

Silver Hope PD377 was built in 1954. Compare her lean and spare and narrow gutted lines with the fuller forms of *Fairweather* PD197, built in the 1960s, and also those of *Forthright* and *Steadfast*.

more distant seining grounds and the need arose for even more substantial boats with comfortable accommodation and greater fish carrying capacity and bigger wheelhouses to hold more sophisticated electronic instruments.

So in 1961 Skipper Philip Morgan had *Graceful* PD343 built for seine netting as far as the Bergen Bank in winter and great lining around Faroe and Rockall in summer.

She was 78ft 3in long with 20ft 8in of beam. Generally bigger all round she was fuller at bow and stern and in the bilges, with lower flatter floors and greater sheer. In profile her stem was more raked and cruiser stern filled out.

Fishroom capacity was around 3,000 cu ft and she carried a Gardner 200hp engine.

Between 1961 and 1967 eight more smaller or larger variations of *Graceful* were built. An interchange of ideas between skippers and builders resulted in new lines plans being drawn for some of them although their hull forms were in general derived from that of *Graceful*.

For instance, the seiner and liner *Daisy* PD433 was 79ft long with fuller bilges and slightly greater beam, whereas the 78ft *Glenugie III* PD347 was based on *Daisy* but was fuller on the quarter to provide buoyancy and space for a bigger deckhouse.

Glenugie III, under Skipper Donald Anderson, rose to fame in 1966 when she became the first British boat to work a herring purse seine. Her achievement proved the viability of this method of fishing and later that year Peterhead skipper Alex John Buchan placed with Irvins the first order from Scotland for a boat specially designed to use the purse net.

Although she looked basically similar to a traditional 1960s seiner trawler,
Vigilant *PD452 was the first boat from a British yard*
especially ordered and designed as a purse seiner for Scottish owners.

First purse seiner.

Named *Vigilant* PD452 she started fishing in 1967 under Skipper William Buchan, son of Skipper Alex John Buchan.

She embodied many innovations for her builders.

Although in general appearance she looked like a traditional seiner trawler, *Vigilant* was one of the most powerful and well equipped wooden boats in Scotland, being full-bodied and heavily built in order to work the enormous purse net and handle the huge catches of some 800 crans of herring which could be made in a single haul.

Her hull form was a development from *Glenugie III*, the lines plan being opened out and expanded generally to produce in *Vigilant* a bigger and fuller lined vessel.

With overall length of 82ft and beam of 22ft 3in and depth from underside of keel to top of deck beam of 12ft 6in, *Vigilant* was longer and beamier and deeper than *Glenugie III*. She had fuller bow and bilges and flatter floors for good catch carrying ability and her beam was carried well aft to give a full stern providing buoyancy and space for holding the purse net which weighed more than five tons. Her fishroom was 33ft long.

Construction was similar to that of *Forthright* but with two additional deck beams of steel joist below the heavy pursing winch.

Vigilant was a chunky solid looking boat which sat in the water well. An elderly fisherman was moved to exclaim '...now isn't yon *Vigilant* the finest looking boatie that you ever clapped eyes on ..'. The fishermen were discerning and knowledgeable critics.

Vigilant had a 410hp Caterpillar engine and carried Norwinch low pressure hydraulic deck machinery including a combined pursing and trawl winch positioned forward of the deckhouse, and a flydragging seine winch which could also be used to work the brailer for emptying the purse seine.

The winches were powered by a Norwinch 85hp pump driven from the main engine. Low pressure hydraulic systems were simple and rugged and provided a powerful heave.

A Rapp 28in diameter power block was hung from a crane fitted on the starboard side of the deckhouse, and a small device called a presswheel was used with the block to increase friction between net and block, thereby hauling the net more quickly and easily.

The pursing gallows was fitted at the starboard bow.

For herring searching *Vigilant* carried Elac Mittel Lodar sonar which indicated the depth of a shoal and its bearing and distance from the boat and its approximate size and density. The tiltable transducer was housed in a plastic ball at the end of a shaft mounted in the boat's bottom and could be retracted into the hull when not in use.

When she was first built *Vigilant* used a purse seine 240 fathoms long and 72 fathoms deep, which took the makers three months to make. It was rigged with 1½ tons of lead weights and 1500 floats. Later she used a net measuring 280 fathoms by 90 fathoms. She has caught as much as 797 crans of herring in one haul.

The wooden vessel *Lunar Bow* PD425, under Skipper Alex John Buchan, worked as a 'bum boat', using a tow line to prevent *Vigilant* from drifting across the net and closing it, and also carrying part of the catch.

Vigilant also worked as a flydragging seiner and herring pair trawler.

Perfection.

Irvins delivered the 78ft seiner and herring pair trawler *Achilles* PD178 to Skipper Andrew Strachan of Peterhead in 1968. Having 22ft of beam she was smaller aft than *Vigilant* but was even fuller forward with lower and more rounded bilges and less hollow floors.

With full, yet satisfying, lines and bright yellow hull she was quite a favourite and one fisherman said '.. there's some would say that *Achilles* is perfection ..'.

Her equipment included Caterpillar 375hp engine and Mastra hydraulic seine and trawl winch. Originally *Achilles* had no power block but in 1970 she was fitted with a Rapp 19R model on an articulated crane designed for hauling herring trawls. With an extra hydraulic

*The author had a purse seining trip with **Vigilant** in 1969 to the herring grounds north-west of the Island of Foula. Here, herring are being brailed out of the net.*

*Achilles PD178 was a little bit fuller aft and finer forward than **Forthright** and **Steadfast**. She was admired for her good looks. Note the articulated crane on which her power block is hung.*

Ugievale II PD105 and **Stanhope II** *PD115 (foreground) under construction.*
*Note **Ugievale II**'s double frames. **Stanhope II** was of slightly*
lighter construction because she was smaller.

cylinder working an extendable section of crane the block could be lowered over the boat's side towards the water and under the net to help in lifting it on board. During her first winter at the herring pair trawling *Achilles* worked in partnership with *Honey Bee* PD110 and *Utilise* PD214 built by Irvins in the 1950s.

She spent six or seven weeks seine netting in the early summer, but during the Shetland herring season she took time away from fishing to work as a herring carrier. She joined five other boats transporting herring landed in Shetland ports down to Fraserburgh for the kippering and canning factories.

Skipper Strachan referred to this herring carrying job as 'fishing for kippers'.

Irvins next built *Ugievale II* PD105 and *Stanhope II* PD115 for Peterhead skippers Arthur Buchan and Peter Strachan.

Ugievale II's lines were based on those of *Achilles* and she was the same size, although to begin with she had no whaleback. Her equipment included Caterpillar 400hp engine and Mastra hydraulic winch and she began life working with five other Peterhead herring pair trawlers in the group named the 'Bix Six'. Early in 1969 they netted 1,000 crans during one night's fishing off Barra Head in the Hebrides.

Stanhope II measured 74ft 4in x 20ft 3in and had a Kelvin 320hp engine and Norwinch hydraulic seine and trawl winch. She was slighter in shape and construction than the full bodied 78 footers. In hull form she was a slightly deeper version of *Prevail* LH444, built in 1966 for Skipper Peter Johnstone of Port Seton.

Stanhope II normally worked seine nets on the Bergen Bank and caught mainly haddock and cod.

Late in 1970 she was fitted with a Rapp 19R power block.

Forthright and *Steadfast* were built after *Ugievale II* and *Stanhope II* and were finer aft and fuller forward than *Achilles* and *Ugievale II*. Next came the 79ft x 22ft 3in *Sparkling Star* PD108 which compared with *Forthright* had finer lines and hollower floors.

Irvins continued to build large, wooden hulled cruiser sterned boats, finishing with the 85ft by 24ft *Sunbeam* INS189 for Skipper William Smith of Lossiemouth in 1978, after which the firm pulled out of boatbuilding.

Other Builders: Cruiser sterned seiners and trawlers.

Successful and influential.

One of the most successful and influential wooden cruiser sterned boats was the seine netter *Argonaut III* KY337. Built by Jones Buckie Shipyard Ltd. in 1969 for Skipper David Smith of Anstruther, she was the highest-earning Scottish seiner for five of the six years which she spent under his command.

Argonaut III's lines were designed by Glasgow naval architects G. L. Watson and Co. Ltd. which was founded in 1873. The firm had designed the 80ft *Shemara* PD235 delivered from Jones in 1964 to Skipper James Pirie of Peterhead.

Following *Shemara*'s building Watson became heavily involved with fishing vessels and by 1980 had provided lines plans for more than ninety boats produced by Scottish yards.

Argonaut III was very refined looking with crisp and fair lines and measured 78ft x 22.25ft. Deck equipment included Mastra hydraulic seine winch and Rapp 19R power block; Skipper Smith had pioneered the use of the power block in Scotland for hauling seine nets when his previous vessel *Argonaut II* KY357 was fitted with a Hydema unit from Norway.

Argonaut III was powered by a Caterpillar 450hp engine coupled through a 4:1 reduction gearbox to a 66in Bruntons propeller, and her fish finders comprised Elac Echograph Superior and Fishlupe.

She fished in the North Sea on grounds such as the Bergen Bank and landed her catches at Aberdeen and Peterhead, and occasionally North Shields. In 1970 she sold her catches for £101,190 to become the first Scottish seiner to earn more than £100,000 in a year. Good catch rates and the rise in fish prices in the early 1970s gave *Argonaut III* a grossing of £219,000 in 1974, a figure better than the earnings of some distant-water trawlers almost twice her size.

Rope reels and the gutting shelter.

In the early 1970s she was the first boat in Scotland to get a gutting shelter and rope storage reels which later became standard equipment in the seine net fleet and made this fishing a safer and less arduous job.

Made of GRP the shelter formed a canopy around the fore side of the deckhouse. For the fishermen gutting the catch it afforded some protection from the weather and from heavy seas which might sweep aboard. It was later replaced by a stronger aluminium structure.

Rope storage reels brought a good degree of automation to working the gear. The traditional method of using winch and rope coiler had occasioned much dangerous manhandling of the ropes.

When the gear was being hauled the coils of rope had to be dragged away from the coiler and arranged along deck ready for shooting away again. Shooting the gear was particularly risky as the man standing near the ropes to ensure that they ran out smoothly was in danger of being pulled overboard in a fouled bight of rope.

These hazards were eliminated by use of the reels which could accommodate all the ropes.

Use of rope reels was instigated in Scotland by Skipper Peter Murray of Anstruther, who with Skipper Smith assisted in their development with the Norwegian manufacturers, Fish and Ships Gear a/s. The two prototype reels supplied to *Argonaut III* each held sixteen coils of 3in rope.

Skipper Smith said 'What we have is complete automation. No-one is required at the winch and reels when hauling the ropes'. The winch hauled the ropes which then travelled via rollers onto the reels, which followed the speed of the winch. Automatic guiding-on

*Skipper David Smith MBE and **Argonaut III** KY337 were successful and influential.
Argonaut III was the highest earning Scottish seiner in the early 1970s
and was the first to have a gutting shelter and seine rope storage reels.*

The two photographs show her as built in 1969, and a few years later after being fitted with the reels and shelter.

gear distributed the rope around the reel evenly. Controls for the reels were below the whaleback. Brakes in the wheelhouse governed the speed of shooting the ropes from the reels.

The reels were hydraulically driven from a small hydraulic pump powered by the main engine. A manual over-ride enabled damaged rope to be guided through a slot in the end flange and onto an auxiliary drum for repair without interrupting the hauling process.

In 1973 a similar set of reels was fitted to the 74ft wooden hulled seiner *Arktos* KY255, built earlier in the year in Norway for Skipper Peter Murray's son Skipper Colin Murray. Her reels were shorter than those on *Argonaut III* and had wheelhouse controls.

During the same year a set of reels of McTaggart Scott make were supplied to the large Peterhead seiner *Viking Deeps* PD75, formerly the Aberdeen trawler *George Craig*.

Use of the reels allowed her to fish with 3¼in ropes which would have been too heavy for the crew to handle in the normal way. Despite the obvious benefits of rope reels, they temporarily lost favour for a year or two owing to the introduction of the rope storage bin as an alternative method of stowing the ropes.

Kallista, a hefty herring trawler.

Some really hefty cruiser sterned boats came from J. and G. Forbes and Co. at Sandhaven.

The 80ft seiner and herring pair trawler *Kallista* FR107 built in 1972 for Skipper George Watt was one of the most substantial and powerful wooden vessels in the British fleet.

Her 23ft beam was broader than that of other boats of similar length and her 850hp engine enabled her to use a larger net and tow through the herring shoals at greater speed in order to increase her catching ability. It also gave

*Built by J. and G. Forbes in 1972 **Kallista** FR107 was one of the most substantial and powerful wooden hulled boats in the British fleet.*

her a free running speed of more than twelve knots to make a quick passage to and from the herring grounds.

She was heavily built to withstand the stress of the large engine and most of her scantlings were as big as, or greater than, those specified by the White Fish Authority for boats of 90ft in length.

In hull form she was full amidships but had a finer entry and flared bow to make it easy on herself when steaming at speed.

Deck beams, main bulkheads, all engine and tank seats and the deckhouse and whaleback were steel, and much of her planking was oak and also iroko which is a hard and durable West African timber able to withstand a good amount of wear and tear.

Bulwarks were of extra height to give better protection for the fishermen working on deck.

Her Caterpillar D398 twelve cylinder engine turned a controllable pitch propeller through a 3.9:1 reduction gearbox. Controllable pitch propellers allow the angle of the blades to be varied so that the engine can be used to maximum efficiency. Blade pitch can be set to near maximum for free running speed, but a shallower pitch gives greater towing power.

The hydraulically powered Jensen combined seine and trawl winch was positioned below the whaleback with the trawl drums set fore-aft forward of the seine barrels. These Danish winches were finding favour in Scotland as they were designed to withstand the heaviest duties required of them aboard the powerful herring trawlers.

A rugged 24in power block from the Carron Company of Falkirk was fitted on an exceptionally robust articulated crane. Trawl gallows were sited at starboard bow and both quarters, and the hull was sheathed with stainless steel plate in way of the gallows.

Kallista's fishroom could hold five hundred crans of herring in boxes. Electronics included Elac Mittel Lodar sonar and the new Decca Mk 21 Navigator which used solid state electronics and micro circuit techniques and was easier to read than the Mk 12.

A nice touch to the boat was her name board. *Kallista* means 'water maiden' and a mermaid was painted on her bows.

The last of the ring netters.

The last of the herring ring netters were built in the early 1970s but they were also equipped for other types of fishing.

With the growth of the pair trawl and purse seine, ring netting along with drift net fishing was on the wane, but in 1972 the herring fleet comprised 33 ring netters, 17 pursers, 61 trawlers and 10 drifters. By 1976 these figures stood at 8 ringers, 26 pursers, 105 trawlers and only 3 drifters.

At the close of World War II ring net vessels had been dainty craft in the 45ft size range, but during the 1950s more were adopting seine netting and prawn trawling between the herring seasons. Experience showed that 58ft to 61ft was an ideal length for these dual purpose boats, large enough to work seine nets and trawls, yet having manoeuvrability for ring netting in restricted waters. Later ring netters were fitted for other modes of fishing and were somewhat larger.

Herd and Mackenzie at Buckie built a fine looking ring netter, scallop dredger and pair trawler in 1971 for Skipper Alistair Jack of Avoch. Named *Monadhliath* INS140, pronounced Mon-lee-ah, after a range of Scottish mountains, she measured 64ft x 19ft and unlike the usual ring netters her fishroom was forward followed by engineroom and cabin.

A Norwinch two drum trawl and scallop dredging winch was positioned on the foredeck and a Norwinch ring net winch forward of the deckhouse. Twin derricks for towing scallop dredges were fitted forward of the deckhouse and the boat's sides were sheathed with stainless steel against abrasion from the dredges.

A ring net brailing derrick was supported on deck by a steel sampson post and trawl gallows were located at the quarters.

Her fishroom had the large hatch characteristic of ring netters. No auxiliary engine was carried and the low pressure hydraulic pump for the winches was belt driven from the forward end of the Gardner 8L3B 230hp propulsion unit.

The transom stern.

Radical departure in design.

The introduction of the transom stern into the seiner trawler fleet was one of the most radical departures in the design of Scottish wooden vessels since the development of the cruiser stern after World War I.

Until the start of the 1970s the majority of skippers were happy with cruiser sterned boats. For some forty years they had proved themselves to be so versatile and easy to handle and were such splendid seaboats, but more fishermen were now favouring the transom stern because it afforded more space aft above and below deck, and some felt that the cleaner underwater lines around the stern produced more speed and towing power.

Design and construction details of the transom stern varied from builder to builder, but basically that part of the hull abaft the sternpost ended square instead of being shaped into the sharp ended cruiser stern.

The beam of the boat was carried further aft and the run of the buttocks flattened out to provide greater width at the after end of the vessel.

Several Scottish yards had delivered transom sterned boats to overseas owners in the 1950s. In 1960 Herd and Mackenzie had foreseen the move towards this design feature in Scotland by building the 37ft prawn trawler *Edindoune* BCK142 which had her wheelhouse forward.

J. and G. Forbes built Scotland's first transom sterned seiner trawler *Constellation* FR294 in 1964 for Skipper Joe Buchan, though she too was of forward wheelhouse configuration.

The 64ft ring netter and scallop dredger Monadhliath INS140 leaving Buckie for her acceptance trials. Note the various derricks for brailing herring, towing scallop dredges, and lifting aboard the cod end of her trawl.

Franchise A87 was one of two transom sterned sister ships built by Gerrard Brothers at Arbroath in 1969. Note the extra space aft afforded by the transom stern.

Stella Maris WK142 being launched from Jones Buckie Shipyard in 1973. Built for Skipper David Cowie she had a Caterpillar 280hp engine, Norlau seine and trawl winch and Kelvin Hughes echosounder. Note her transom stern and trawl gallows.

Highland Queen LH62 being launched at Dunbar in 1972. Weatherhead and Blackie was founded at Port Seton in the 1950s, but later moved to Dunbar where it could build boats under cover.

Other builders adopted the transom stern during the following five or six years and as the 1970s progressed boats with this feature began to outnumber those with cruiser sterns.

Although some were of stern fishing layout with the superstructure forward, the majority were of similar arrangement to the traditional cruiser sterned seiner trawler both on deck and below.

Early examples of these included the 50ft sister ships *Franchise* A87 and *Fruitful* A99, built by Gerrard Brothers at Arbroath in 1969 for Skippers Jack Reid and Gordon Cowie of Aberdeen.

With lines drawn by G. L. Watson they had a beam of 17ft 9in and fittings included Caterpillar 200hp engine, Mastra winch and Rapp power block. They were the first transomers to come from Gerrards, which had started building fishing boats in 1955.

Eyemouth Boatbuilding Company, after building two or three vessels with transom sterns, delivered the seiner trawler *Star of Hope* LH260 to skipper Peter Jarron of Port Seton in 1970. A stout and roomy 60 footer with 20ft beam she was built from a new lines plan designed by yard director James Evans. Mackay Boatbuilders at Arbroath built its first transomer the 61ft *Argus* AH30 in 1971, for the four Teviotdale brothers.

J. and G. Forbes was one of the most productive builders of transom sterned boats in the early 1970s. The 80ft *Radiant Star* FR127, built in 1973 for Skipper Alex Wiseman of Gardenstown, was a hefty chunk of a seiner trawler with 23ft beam and Caterpillar 565hp engine and controllable pitch propeller.

Smaller transomers included the 55ft by 18ft *Stella Maris* WK142 designed by G. L. Watson and built by Jones Buckie Shipyard in 1973 for Skipper David Cowie. She was the first new boat to join the Helmsdale fleet for about twelve years. Down at Dunbar, Weatherhead and Blackie launched *Highland Queen* LH62 in 1972 for skipper David Fairburn. She measured 54ft 6in with 18ft beam and had a GRP whaleback.

English owners interested.

Almost all Scottish yards have built boats for England.

James Noble (Fraserburgh) Ltd. delivered the transom sterned seiner trawler *Venus* FR79 to Skipper Jacob Cole of Whitby in 1971. Yorkshire fishermen worked heavy inshore trawls over rough ground and liked the Noble boats for their sturdiness and good towing characteristics.

The arrival of *Venus* in Whitby caused quite a stir as she was so much stouter with fuller lines than other seiner trawlers in the port's fleet at that time.

With overall length of 54ft and beam of 18ft *Venus* was equipped with Gardner 230hp engine, Sutherland six speed belt driven seine and trawl winch and Beccles coiler. She had trawl gallows at starboard bow and quarter and a stout gilson derrick forward of the deckhouse for lifting the cod end aboard. The two trawl warps could be clipped to a steel towing eye fitted on the after end of the deckhouse in order to give more precise control over towing operations.

Wheelhouse instruments included Kelvin Hughes MS44 recording echosounder, type 17 radar, Sailor radio-telephone and Decca Navigator.

Mechanical chain steering gear was fitted, and deckhouse and whaleback were steel.

Venus FR79 *arriving in Whitby after her delivery trip from James Noble (Fraserburgh) Ltd.*
The yard built a number of sturdy cruiser and transom sterned seiner trawlers
for Yorkshire fishermen.

Chapter 3
A GREATER ACCEPTANCE OF STEEL

Fishermen often discuss the relative merits of wooden and steel boats. Both materials have advantages and drawbacks.

Timber has been used throughout boatbuilding history. Providing that the timber was of excellent quality and the building craftsmanship good, a wooden boat can last a long time and several aged sixty years and more were still fishing in the 1970s.

Some of the oldest working full time in Scottish waters were based at Arbroath. The 43ft *Fortuna* AH153 built as *Isabella* by James Weir at Arbroath in 1890 was a typical small sailing fifie. Later she was converted to motor power and given wheelhouse and winch and other up-to-date fittings but was withdrawn from fishing in 1976. She has since been restored as the sailing fifie *Isabella Fortuna* AH153.

With a handful of exceptions, steel had been used only for larger trawlers and some steam drifters.

Among some fifty boats between 40ft and 90ft built for Scottish owners in 1969 only six or seven were steel. Onwards from 1969 there was a greater acceptance of steel within this size range.

Pursing and pair trawling called for vessels near on 90ft long, with greater sea range and catching and carrying capabilities. Many were built of steel, as good quality large scantlings for big wooden boats became difficult to find.

At the same time, cutbacks in demand for other commercial craft caused shipyards with steel ship-building skills to compete for fishing vessel orders. The price of steel boats became more competitive owing to modern welding and fabrication techniques and the rising cost of prime timber. Providing hull shape and other design features were right, steel boats could be as seaworthy as wooden ones of similar size.

Homogeneous.

Steel is of a uniform quality so that the components of a boat are welded together to form a very strong homogeneous single-piece unit. Well-built steel craft do not leak and are able to withstand quite hefty knocks and dents without loss of strength.

The material can be fabricated into complex structures, so steel boats can have refinements such as a bulbous or semi bulbous bow. Ballast tanks and fish tanks are incorporated easily because the hull forms their outer walls. Steel vessels can be modified or lengthened without being weakened and are able to withstand vibrations produced by bigger engines.

Powerful alternating current electrical systems are more safely installed as they can be earthed properly.

Because steel is consistent in quality the plates and shapes are thinner than the scantlings of a wooden vessel thereby providing more internal space.

The disadvantages of steel were being understood and overcome. Corrosion caused by rust and electrolysis could be counteracted by careful use of correctly treated shipbuilding quality steel and protective coatings, and the fitting of sacrificial anodes.

The magnetic affects of steel caused some wheelhouse instruments to malfunction but this could be remedied. Condensation problems and noise transmission could also be reduced.

Some skippers felt that steel boats were more suitable for working the new fishing methods. Pair trawling was very strenuous and wooden vessels could receive nasty damage should they bump into their partner boats.

The heavy gear and trawl doors used by single-boat demersal trawlers could also be harmful.

Others still preferred wooden hulled boats and the builders of these had full order books. Scottish wooden hulled vessels were praised all over the world for their excellent seakeeping and handling qualities.

Although wooden boats were vulnerable to leaks and to attack from wet rot fungus and worm, and timber could be of variable quality with internal weaknesses, these faults could be counteracted by larger scantlings and the careful choice of timber and good construction and treatment.

Hulls could be sheathed with steel or plastic in the places where abrasion and damage was likely.

Colossal demand.

During the early 1970s there was a colossal demand for steel boats in the 70ft to 90ft size range, particularly among the herring trawling and purse seining fleets of north-east Scotland. More than thirty were built for Peterhead alone between 1968 and 1977.

By 1973 at least fifteen British firms as far apart as Campbeltown, London, Hull and Aberdeen were building steel boats for Scottish owners and several skippers ordered steel boats from the Continent.

Some steel vessels broadly resembled their wooden counterparts in shape, although they did not always have the subtleties of line associated with wooden boats owing to the different working properties of the two materials. Other steel craft departed quite radically in shape because of alternative and often more economical construction techniques.

Some early steel seiner trawlers.

An early example of a steel vessel built to replace a wooden one was the 79ft 9in *Fairweather IV* PD107, delivered from the Fairmile Construction Company at Berwick in 1969 to Skipper John Alex Buchan of Peterhead.

Of round bilge form with cruiser stern and raked stem, and beam of 22ft she had similar equipment to her wooden hulled contemporaries, namely Caterpillar 400hp engine, Lister 22hp auxiliary engine, Mastra hydraulic seine and trawl winch, Rapp power block and Elac echosounder and Fishlupe. She was one of the group of Peterhead vessels known as the 'Big Five' which worked together at the herring pair trawling.

Challenger PD104, built in 1970 by Richard Dunston Ltd. of Hessle in Yorkshire for Skipper Andrew Strachan of Peterhead, was of similar size, measuring 79ft 6in x 22ft and fitted with Caterpillar 400hp engine, Mastra winch and Rapp block, but she concentrated on seine net fishing from her home port. Dunston had pioneered the building of all-welded ships in the UK during World War II and subsequently produced the first fully welded trawler.

The Start of Campbeltown Shipyard

Campbeltown Shipyard, which was to become the most productive builder of steel fishing boats in the UK, was officially opened at Campbeltown in the Mull of Kintyre in 1968.

In 1970 local skipper James McDonald took delivery of the yard's first completion, the 50ft stern trawler *Crimson Arrow* CN30. Instead of having round bilges her transom sterned welded steel hull was built on the double chine principle, in that in cross section the underwater shape of the hull is not curved but rises from keel to topsides in a series of straight lines which meet at sharp angles.

This is a simple and economical method of steel boatbuilding as the frames require no shaping into curves except at the forward end of the boat and the plates are bent into single fore-aft curves rather than into more complex double curves.

Designed for prawn trawling and scallop dredging *Crimson Arrow* was powered by a Dorman 142hp engine driving the propeller in a fixed nozzle from the Kort Propulsion Co. Ltd. Designed to give increased towing power a nozzle is a cylindrical ring of aerofoil section fitted around the propeller.

Yard No.4 the trawler *Steadfast* LH90, built for Skipper John Horne of Eyemouth, took to the water late in 1970.

Measuring 49ft 11½in x 17ft x 9ft moulded depth she had a double chined hull with transom stern and raked flat bar stem. Of conventional seiner trawler layout with deckhouse aft she was robust and roomy for her size with deep freeboard and bulwarks and good headroom below deck.

*The 79ft 6in steel boat **Challenger** PD104 leaving Peterhead for a seine netting trip. Note the shape of her cruiser stern which is less pointed at deck level than that of a wooden boat.*

***Steadfast** LH90 nearing completion at Campbeltown Shipyard. Note her double chined steel hull and Kort steering nozzle.*

Propulsion was provided by a Cummins NH 250 M six cylinder engine producing 190hp at 1800 rpm coupled through a Twin Disc 3.83:1 reduction and reverse gearbox to a 48in diameter propeller housed in a Kort steering nozzle. Unlike the fixed nozzle this rotated about the vertical axis and also functioned as a rudder.

The first 'Campbeltown 80s'.

In 1972 Campbeltown entered the larger fishing boat market with the 80ft seiner trawlers *Argosy* INS79 and *Ajax* INS82, built for Skippers Andrew and William Campbell who came from a long established Lossie-mouth fishing family.

Skipper William Campbell collaborated with the builders on the design of the two boats. One of Scotland's most skilful and highly respected seine net fishermen he was always willing to look at ways of improving vessel efficiency and catch quality and had been awarded the MBE for his services to the fishing industry.

He was a great believer in the superiority of Scottish cruiser sterned boats from the point of view of seaworthiness and gear handling ability.

Argosy and *Ajax* were of round bilge form with cruiser stern, raked soft nose stem, and whaleback. Their clean graceful lines were not unlike those of wooden vessels.

They were of traditional seiner trawler layout with deckhouse aft, and below deck subdivided from forward into net store, fishroom, engineroom and crew's accommodation. This well proven design was combined with the most advanced steel boatbuilding techniques to produce two vessels which were the forerunners of some twenty-one cruiser sterned 80 footers built by Campbeltown during the subsequent twelve years.

In the light of the working experience with *Argosy*

Argosy INS79 was the first of the acclaimed series of 80ft cruiser sterned steel vessels to come from Campbeltown Shipyard.

47

some minor alterations were made to *Ajax* which illustrated the close co-operation which took place between the builders and Skipper Campbell, and their attention to detail.

With overall length of 79ft 11in, beam of 22ft and moulded depth amidships of 11ft *Argosy* was built throughout of electrically welded Lloyds tested mild steel. Plates and shapes were shot blasted and primed and then coated on both sides with Metalife corrosion resistant composition, the latter combating the chemical process which causes rust to develop.

She was powered by the recently introduced Caterpillar D346 TA engine which developed 480hp at 1800 rpm to drive the Bruntons 64in diameter propeller through a 5.17:1 reduction gearbox.

No 24v alternators were fitted because a simplified electrical system utilised only the 110v generators and two banks of batteries. It had been developed by the White Fish Authority's Industrial Development Unit to meet all electrical requirements.

Gear handling equipment included a Jensen seine and trawl winch with trawl drums fitted fore-aft, a Carron 20in power block on a single reach crane with rotary actuator, and a Beccles rope coiler.

Able to carry six hundred boxes of white fish the fishroom was insulated with Solarfoam, a material which had hitherto been used for cavity wall insulation in the house building trade.

New echosounder.

Electronic instruments included the new Kingfisher II fishfinding system from Kelvin Hughes, comprising MS44 recording echosounder with BL1 scale expansion unit.

Echosounders were now giving more useful and comprehensive information about the situation below a vessel and the MS44 offered 'white line' and 'grey line' presentation on the recording paper.

With 'white line' the seabed profile was shown as a thin black line above a white zone. Fish close to the seabed gave echoes causing a thickening of the black line which stood out clearly against the white area.

However, in bad weather, the black line could break up and make fish detection difficult. 'Grey line' could overcome this problem as the seabed echoes produced a grey zone against which fish echoes showed black.

The BL1 equipment presented expanded recordings on the wide paper of the MS44 alongside the normal recording thereby giving all the fish finding information on the one display unit.

Minor modifications aboard *Ajax* included lowering the port fuel tank in the engine room and lowering the cabin floor to give more headroom.

Ajax and rope storage bins.

Early in 1973 *Ajax* became the first Scottish seiner to use seine rope storage bins.

From the Beccles coiler the ropes were allowed to fall through circular hatches in the deck down into the two bins which were arranged in the forward end of the fishroom and separated from the rest of the fishroom by stanchions and pound boards.

The idea was developed by Skipper Campbell and the WFA's IDU with trials being held on board *Ajax* around the same time as *Argonaut III* was experimenting with rope storage reels.

Bins had the advantage over reels in that they were simple and cheap to install and involved no mechanical parts or maintenance and used up less deck space.

Should a piece of rope need repair it was not allowed to fall into the bin but kept on deck for splicing.

Argosy was also fitted with bins and by the middle of 1973 boatyards and engineers were coping with a rush of orders for similar conversions. For the following three or four years bins were preferred to reels. At least one skipper cancelled an order for reels in favour of the bins.

Pocket Trawlers

The 'Spinningdale Class'.

During the early 1970s Aberdeen built up an efficient little fleet of some twenty-five 86ft 'pocket' trawlers, so

*The first three 'Campbeltown 80s' lying in Buckie. They are **Argosy** INS79, **Ajax** INS82 and **Opportune** BCK105. Built for Skipper George Murray of Buckie in 1973 **Opportune** had similar engine and deck machinery to the other two, but her deckhouse was slightly higher and she had an Atlas 720 echosounder with fishlupe.*

__Pisces__ A193 was a Spinningdale Mk1 'pocket' trawler. Note her stout bipod foremast carrying the gilson blocks below the crosstree. She had trawl gallows at the starboard side only.

named to distinguish them from the larger white fish vessels based at the port.

The pocket trawlers were handy economical successors to the older 115ft class of vessel and in the main they were part owned by their skippers in partnership with trawler companies. They made weekly trips to Shetland and Orkney and the Scottish west coast and proved themselves to be efficient and seakindly. Twenty-one were built by John Lewis and Sons Ltd. at Aberdeen and became known as the 'Spinningdale' class, named after the *Spinningdale* A473 built in the late 1960s.

A beamier version the Spinningdale Mk 1 was introduced in 1969 with the completion of *David John* A169 and during the subsequent four years another dozen Mk1s were built for Aberdeen.

With round bilges, transom stern and flared soft nose bow they were arranged for starboard side fishing only and boxed their catches at sea.

With a beam of 21ft 3in the second Spinningdale Mk 1 was *Pisces* A193 built in 1971 for Skipper Harry Duncan in association with the Burwood Fishing Co.

She incorporated several new ideas in deck layout. In place of a single pole mast she carried a bipod structure which gave more room and consequently greater safety and ease of movement on deck.

Gilson blocks were hung from the crosstree of the bipod mast, and the fore derrick was fitted to the starboard leg of the mast. A gutting machine was positioned forward of the fishroom hatch. Part of the deckhouse was extended to the port rail providing more spacious and comfortable accommodation.

She also had a larger engine than the earlier Spinningdales, namely an air starting Mirrlees Black-stone ETSL6MGR which gave 600hp at 706 rpm and turned the propeller through a 2.5:1 reduction gearbox to give a speed of eleven knots. Compressed air was the usual means of starting lower revving engines.

Tanks in the engineroom held a total of 24 tons of fuel to give a sea endurance of twelve days.

Two Lister 32.25hp auxiliary engines each provided power for a 15kW a. c. alternator, a bilge and general service pump and an air compressor.

Alternating current generators, known as alternators, are smaller and easier to obtain than direct current systems and can operate domestic equipment, but need a constant speed power source. They are also safer in steel boats as they can be suitably earthed.

Placed forward of the deckhouse the Norwinch low pressure hydraulic winch had two main drums and two small auxiliary barrels. It could carry 750 fathoms of 2½in wire on each drum and was powered by a Norwinch P37 pump belt driven from the fore end of the main engine.

Two echosounders.

Made of aluminium the wheelhouse was flared at front and sides to give more internal space and provide a better view onto deck.

Skipper Duncan liked to trawl near to the edge of hard ground and the wheelhouse was fitted with a range of fishfinding and position plotting equipment including two echosounders, a fishlupe, and Decca Track Plotter and Navigator.

Spinningdale Mk11.

The Spinningdales quickly demonstrated their catching power and in 1973 Lewis introduced the improved Mk11 model with greater beam and carrying capacity, and more powerful engine, the first being *Strathclova* A734 for Skipper Alec Simpson.

Her beam of 22ft gave her a sturdier look and allowed for a bigger deckhouse with the wheelhouse more flared.

Her Mirrlees Blackstone engine provided 636hp and drove no auxiliary equipment so all its power was available for steaming and towing.

A 35kW alternator and the hydraulic pump for the Norwinch winch were powered from a Gardner 119hp auxiliary engine, with a smaller Gardner driving another alternator and an air compressor. Bilge and general service pumps and another air compressor were electrically driven.

An 86ft Spinningdale hull under construction upside down.
This particular hull became the trawler and great-line vessel
Dew-genen-ny *PZ185 built for Cornish owners in 1975.*
The unusual name is Cornish for 'God With Us'.

Prefabricated.

Lewis used prefabricated construction methods for the Spinningdales. The hulls were built upside down which allowed for down-hand welding.

First the deck was laid and then the framework, bulkheads and engine bearers erected thereupon and the shell plating done. Then the hull was cut into sections and taken by lorry to the slipway for re-assembly and completion the right way up.

Although named 'pocket' trawlers they differed in shape from their bigger counterparts. Prior to 1960 or so the latter were generally full and flat bottomed amidships for carrying ability and finer at the ends for speed when making long trips, but some tended to push their noses down and not rise very easily.

Therefore the Spinningdales reverted back to the steam drifter type of hull with rising floors amidships and fuller at the ends for better seakeeping, but were transom sterned for ease of construction.

They were built of Lloyds tested steel, which meant that its composition had been analysed to ensure it was of good standard.

Seiner trawler versions.

Two 86ft sister ships *Seringa PD95 and Sundari* PD93 built in 1972 for Skippers John and William Morgan of Peterhead were the first seiner trawler versions of the Mk1 Spinningdale class. They had the same hull form, but layout and fittings were suitable for seine net fishing and herring pair trawling.

First to be completed was *Seringa* which handled well during her sea trials and had an easy and steady movement.

She was powered by a Mirrlees Blackstone air starting engine of 600hp at 706 rpm coupled to the propeller through a 2.5:1 reduction gearbox to give a speed of some eleven knots.

Provision was made to run the engine at 200 rpm when seining.

The first of the beamier Mk11 seiner trawlers were *Salamis* PD142 and *Budding Rose* PD84 built in 1974 for Skippers Tommy Milne and James Bruce of Peterhead.

In 1975 a smaller seiner trawler based on Spinningdale lines, the 75ft *Hesperus* BF219, was delivered to Skipper Michael Watt of Macduff. She was the first of three sister ships which worked together at the herring pair trawling, the other two being *Vesper* BF220 and *Lorena* BF227 built for Skipper Watt's brother George and their cousin Alexander West.

Hesperus was a neat little vessel with agreeable lines and orderly layout. She was 75ft 5½in long overall with beam of 20ft 4in and moulded depth of 10ft 6in.

Her engine was the first of its type in a Scottish boat being a Deutz Kracko SBF12M716U high speed water cooled twelve cylinder Vee-form air starting diesel providing 460hp at 1500 rpm, coupled to a Stone Manganese propeller through a Reintjes gearbox of 5:1 reduction ratio.

Small and light for its power it was 82in long and weighed some 4,409 lbs. *Hesperus* also had the first powerful 28in power block from the Lossie Hydraulic Company which had been founded about two years previously to manufacture a range of robust deck equipment including rope reels and power blocks.

Purse seiner from Holland.

A number of Continental yards built pair trawlers and purse seiners for Scottish skippers. The Dutch firm of Maaskant Macinefabriek delivered the steel purser trawler *Comrade* FR122 in 1973 to Skipper Andrew Tait of Fraserburgh.

Early the following year she demonstrated her catching power when she came into Mallaig with 850 crans of herring caught in one shot of her purse seine. Pursing had increased dramatically during the preceding year or two. In 1973 Scotland owned eighteen purse seiners whose landings accounted for nearon a third of the total herring catch landed by UK vessels at Scottish ports, as against a quarter in 1972.

Rich fishings.

Rich fishings in the Minches led to the phenomenal rise of the remote West Highland village of Mallaig to become the top herring port in Europe, with landings in 1973 worth almost £3 million representing a third of the value of Britain's total herring catch.

In just a few years the Scots had developed phenomenal skill in purse seining and had given deep thought to all aspects of the fishery from searching for herring to improving catch quality. The colossal catching potential of the purse seine led to a demand for larger comprehensively equipped steel vessels able to work bigger nets and carry more fish. Purse seines were now some 300 fathoms long and 95 deep and of stouter construction than earlier nets.

Modern pursers further increased their capabilities by carrying pelagic pair trawls in addition to purse seines, ready to use as dictated by the weather and distribution of the herring shoals.

Comrade represented the state of the art in purser design in the early 1970s. Measuring 89ft 2in x 23ft 8in x 12ft 6in she was of all welded steel construction with transom stern, raked soft nose stem and semi bulbous bow. The latter consists of a bulge in the stem below the waterline and is designed to reduce pitching and increase speed.

She carried chilled seawater tanks, known as CSW tanks, in which to keep herring in good condition. Built as an integral part of the hull forward of the engineroom the three insulated steel tanks held in total some four hundred crans of herring in seawater cooled by the addition of ice. The water was circulated at intervals to prevent temperature layering. Each tank had its own

Hesperus BF219 on a wintery day in Torry Dock in Aberdeen following her completion at the John Lewis yard. Her Deutz engine was the first of its type in a Scottish boat.

Comrade FR122 coming into Mallaig on a snowy morning early in 1974 with a catch of 840 crans of herring taken in one shot of her purse seine. Mallaig was then the top herring port in Europe.

Comrade FR122 in the dry dock in Peterhead. Note her semi bulbous bow and the position of her bow thruster. The Dutch firm of Maaskant Macinefabriek has built a number of purse seiners for Scotland.

hatch and the catch was discharged by brailer. Forward of the tanks a dry fishroom fitted with steel stanchions and aluminium pound boards and insulated with foam lined with steel enabled herring to be carried dry in bulk or in boxes with ice.

Side thrusters.

Comrade's manoeuvrability for working her purse seine was greatly improved by the use of side thrusters. Made by Brunvoll of Norway they consisted of propellers mounted in tunnels fitted athwartships through the hull at bow and stern. They allowed the boat to move sideways thereby dispensing with the need for a helper boat.

They prevented her from drifting over and closing the net when hauling or when taking the catch aboard and from entangling the main propeller in the fishing gear.

The photograph of *Comrade* in dry dock shows the bow thruster just behind her semi bulbous bow.

Karmoy Mek Verksted of Norway supplied almost all the high pressure hydraulic deck machinery including combination purse and trawl winch, boom swinger, boom lifter, flydragging seine net winch and windlass.

Positioned to port abaft the whaleback the purse and trawl winch had two pairs of drums, one for trawl warp and the other for purse wire, so *Comrade* could work either method as required.

Fitted with its own drive shaft and hydraulic motor each pair of drums could operate independently.

A Triplex net winch from Bjorshol Mek Verksted of Norway was set to starboard of the deckhouse. It hauled the net through three rubber coated cylinders and was used in conjunction with a Triplex transport roller which guided the purse net into the storage bin on the after deck. Herring was transferred from net to boat by means of a Karmoy 14in submersible fish pump which sucked the catch through a flexible hose to a fish-and-water separator on deck and thence to the fish tanks or fishroom. It enabled the catch to be taken aboard far more quickly than by brailer.

Sonar was invaluable for herring searching and

Comrade carried Elac Super Lodar sonar with LAZ44 Sonarscope. The Sonarscope presented echoes on a cathode ray tube screen and showed their true bearing from the boat.

Comrade was powered by a Mirrlees Blackstone air starting diesel of 750hp at 900 rpm, coupled to a 72in diameter Liaaen controllable pitch propeller through a Reintjes 2.83:1 reduction gearbox. Hydraulic pumps for the deck machinery, fish pump, and the 80hp bow thruster and 105hp stern thruster were powered from the engine's forward end through a Karmoy single input multi output gearbox. A 110v generator was belt driven from the forward extension shaft.

Another 110v generator, an air compressor and hydraulic pumps for emergency retrieval of the fishing gear were driven from a Lister 75hp auxiliary engine.

Two pumps for bilge and general uses and a third for circulating water in the CSW tanks were powered by electric motors. Five thousand gallons of fuel oil and a thousand gallons of fresh water were carried.

In addition to the sonar the wheelhouse was equipped with Elac LAZ71 echosounder with Fishlupe, Sailor T122 R105 SSB radiotelephone and 142 VHF radiotelephone, Decca Mk 21 Navigator, RM914 radar and 450 autopilot, Woodsons talk-back system, Tenfjord hydraulic steering gear, Ben log, Wynstruments blade type window wiper, and a Speich revolving screen.

Single Side Band, or SSB, radios provided better voice communication and a more efficient ship-to-shore service.

A cabin for the skipper was abaft the wheelhouse and a gas cooker was fitted in the roomy galley-cum-messdeck.

Naval Architects

Independent firms of naval architects were playing a greater role in the fishing industry.

Scotland's fleet of steel seiner trawlers was enhanced during the 1970s by a series of 86ft vessels designed by Tynedraft Design Ltd. of Newcastle upon Tyne.

The first was *Shemara* PD78 delivered in 1973 from John R. Hepworth and Co. (Hull) Ltd. to Skipper James Pirie of Peterhead.

Vigorous and prosperous.

Skipper Pirie did much to develop herring pair trawling into the vigorous and prosperous industry which it had become in the early 1970s. A chance meeting in North Shields with Tynedraft's chairman David Ross prompted Skipper Pirie to ask the firm to design his new vessel.

Tynedraft carried out the entire design project from preparation of hull lines to the decor in the accommodation, but worked in close co-operation with Skipper Pirie whose ideas and preferences were incorporated throughout.

In all some fifteen seiner trawlers were built to *Shemara*'s lines, but fittings varied in accordance with their owners' wishes. Almost all were ordered by Peterhead skippers who were replacing their existing boats with larger more powerful craft able to catch and carry more fish.

Owing to the swing towards pelagic and demersal trawling by vessels of 86ft they were designed chiefly as trawlers, but were also capable of seine net fishing.

Of round bilge form with transom stern and raked soft nose stem they were big boats with high carrying capacity and registered length of 79ft 11in, beam of 22ft 6in and moulded depth of 12ft. Boats below 80ft registered length are classed as Inshore Fishing Vessels and qualified for more generous financial help towards their building than was available to larger vessels.

Compared with wooden boats of similar age and length the Tynedraft boats had deeper bilges and lower, flatter less hollow floors, and a greater flare to the bow. Although they were of fuller form they were sufficiently fine forward to make good speed.

In addition to *Shemara*, Hepworth built *Juneve III* PD215, *Morning Dawn* PD195 and *Constant Friend* PD83.

Beside the Thames.

Five Tynedraft 86ft seiner trawlers came from the London firm of Cubow Ltd. It was a curious experience to see fishing vessels for Scotland under construction beside the river Thames. Named *Calvados* PD205, *Starlight* PD150, *Unity* PD209, *Day Dawn II* PD136 and *Golden Dawn* PD211 these were all completed in 1975.

I came to know *Unity* the best. Built for Skipper John McLean she started life herring pair trawling off the Isle of Man in partnership with *Starlight*.

Commensurate with the move towards greater flexibility she carried trawl winch, seine winch, net drum, net winch with transport roller, anchor windlass, boom swinger and cargo winch. A net drum is used for hauling aboard the trawl and can store it ready for shooting away again, thereby reducing the chance of snagging.

The semi-ring main hydraulic system enabled the motors in any one deck unit to be driven from the variable delivery pump powered from the main engine through a 3:1 step up gearbox. Pressure controls adjusted oil flow to meet the demand of the particular unit in use.

For seining she carried a rope coiler and storage bins.

Unity's entire propulsion system including air starting six cylinder 660hp 413 rpm engine with controllable pitch propeller and fixed nozzle was manufactured by B&W Alpha from Denmark.

Around this time a number of skippers chose this medium speed engine for its durability and robust design and low maintenance costs.

Working as a partnership, *Unity* and *Morning Dawn* were among the first large Scottish boats to pair-trawl for cod successfully. The method could have more catching power than the seine net as the gear could be kept open longer and could be worked over rugged ground. Hauls could amount to around a thousand boxes for trips of a week or less.

During the mid to late 1970s it was to provide a lucrative fishery at a time when herring catching was severely curtailed.

The mid 70s crisis.

Things began to go wrong for many Scottish fishermen during the mid 1970s.

Unity PD209 was designed in Newcastle upon Tyne and built in London for Skipper John McLean of Peterhead.

Golden Dawn PD211 was one of five Tynedraft 86ft steel seiner trawlers built in London for Scottish skippers in the 1970s. Note her roomy deck and transom stern.

57

Monday 31st March 1975. Part of the fleet of eighty boats blockading Aberdeen as part of the inshore fishermen's protest against the political and economic situation in the mid 1970s. In all some 870 boats blockaded Scottish ports.

Although the value of landings by British vessels at Scottish ports reached a record £64 million in 1974 the growth in gross earnings began to be overtaken by tough increases in operating costs.

With fuel prices increasing threefold between 1973 and 1974, and a bothersome rise in all other expenses, some vessels began to run into serious financial trouble.

Difficulties were further compounded by poor catch rates and bad weather. Demand for fish took a downward turn towards the end of 1974 and the year closed with fishermen fearing for the future of their industry. Boatyards began to feel the disquiet, with few orders for new boats.

The Blockade.

Early in 1975 fishermen in England and Scotland expressed their worries by blockading the ports. Their main concerns were to protect their markets against low priced imports of fish, press for the extension of Britain's territorial limits and to secure a revision of the European Community's Common Fisheries Policy regarding rights of access of member states to each other's coastal waters.

The blockade was lifted after Government assurance that the fishermen's interests would be protected concerning fishing limits and the CFP re-negotiation.

Disastrous.

Much of 1975 was disastrous for the fishermen.

For the first time in many years the fleet's gross earnings showed a drop from the preceding year, falling by £5 million to £59 million. A decline in catches and quayside prices was aggravated by ongoing increases in running costs.

Deep sea trawlers were badly affected with only one or two operating at a profit by mid year and about a quarter of Aberdeen's trawler fleet was withdrawn from fishing.

At the same time there were fears that many newer seiners would end the year in deficit. It was estimated that their running costs had risen by some sixty to eighty per cent since the close of 1973, yet they were finding a scarcity of fish in all areas.

Whereas catches of eight hundred boxes had been made by larger seiners earlier in the decade they were lucky to have six hundred in 1975.

In the event, the despondency lifted somewhat towards the end of 1975 when prices and catch rates began to improve and the year ended with indications that the uplift would continue.

Tragedy.

Several tragic and bizarre things happened during the 1970s. Most unhappy of all was the loss of a number of boats with all hands. And the economic upheaval in the mid decade forced the closure of several boatyards, with half-built vessels left on their slipways.

During atrocious weather several boats vanished without trace. But in October 1974, in what was reported to be a fairly rough sea and a Force 5 to 6 wind, the 85ft steel trawler *Trident* PD111 and her crew of seven disappeared just south of the Pentland Firth while going home to Peterhead from the west coast.

The Dept. of Trade conducted a Court of Inquiry to try and determine the possible cause of her loss. Evidence was given by all those who had any connection with *Trident* or had been associated with her design and building and by people with knowledge of the weather and sea conditions in the area where she foundered.

Witnesses gave some four hundred thousand words of testimony and the Inquiry lasted ten days. The official finding of the Court was that 'It is probable that *Trident* took aboard a sea or succession of seas and foundered, the precise causes of the casualty being unascertainable. The Court considers it probable that deficient stability in her design contributed to her foundering'.

Skipper David Tait, who had not been aboard the boat at the time, was considered by the Court to be in no way to blame for the loss.

Stability.

Assessment of *Trident*'s design characteristics were largely arrived at by the detailed study of her one sister ship the Peterhead registered *Silver Lining* PD82.

The case aroused a great deal of discussion in fishing circles and did much to further the appreciation that adequate stability is one of the most important features contributing to fishing vessel safety.

Stability describes the ability of a boat to return to the upright after being heeled over by an outside force.

Determining the stability characteristics of fishing boats involves naval architects in an enormous amount of measurement and mathematical calculation and drawing. They can easily design vessels with acceptable standards of stability. It would be simple enough to produce a boat with more than ample stability, but her movements would be so violent that it would be impossible to sail on her, so naval architects must find a happy compromise between seakindliness and high stability characteristics.

Stability of a given boat is influenced by a multitude of interacting factors but basically it is governed by hull

Silver Lining PD82 leaving Peterhead on her trip to Devon to be lengthened.

shape, the placing and weight of equipment, loading conditions, amount of freeboard, the weather —tightness or otherwise of doors and hatches and other openings, the extent of enclosed spaces above deck and also the weather and seamanship and methods of handling the fishing gear.

There is no guarantee that a boat with good stability features will not capsize as the sea can overpower anything, and there have been vessels with poor characteristics which have survived for years.

Impossible.

It is impossible to define a clear-cut dividing line between stability and instability or further to say that all boats falling below that dividing line are unsafe and those above guaranteed to be safe.

In the 1960s the Inter Governmental Maritime Consultative Organisation (IMCO) drew up a set of stability criteria which it recommended be met by new fishing vessels over 24m registered length under the various conditions of loading which they could expect to undergo during a normal fishing trip.

The criteria were arrived at by the study of stability features of vessels which had foundered and of those which were successful in operation.

These investigations revealed that those with characteristics below a certain level were prone to capsizing, but IMCO's basic recommendations were intended to have a safety margin.

Until this time few fishing vessels had been subject to stability assessment. Design of the smaller class of boat had been an artistic rather than a scientific exercise, but when the stability of existing Scottish vessels came to be measured the majority were found to be above the IMCO recommendations.

However, boats failing to meet the IMCO standards were not uncommon in the British Isles and overseas, and usually remedies could be found.

In 1975 the Dept. of Trade introduced legislation[1] requiring that all fishing vessels with a registered length of 12m and over meet IMCO's recommendations, although preparation for this ruling was well in hand before the loss of *Trident* and for some five years or so a number of builders had already ensured that their boats complied with the IMCO criteria.

Righting levers.

One of the most critical factors affecting stability is the 'GZ' or righting lever which occurs when the boat heels to port or starboard. Very basically this represents the horizontal distance between the centre of gravity through which the weight of the boat acts downwards and the centre of buoyancy through which her buoyancy acts upwards. When the boat heels these two forces combine to pull her upright again.

The centre of gravity remains in a fixed position on the centreline above the keel but the position of the centre of buoyancy and hence the length of the righting lever constantly changes according to angles of heel, but the greater its length the better the vessel's ability to return to the vertical.

The righting lever increases in length up to a certain angle of heel but decreases as the vessel heels further. On most boats it eventually diminishes to nothing and beyond this point the boat will capsize. One of IMCO's stability criteria asked that the length of 'GZ' should be at its greatest at an angle of heel preferably exceeding 30 degrees but not less than 25 degrees.[2]

Cut in half.

Silver Lining, built in 1973 for Skipper Peter Johnstone of Port Seton, had similar lines to *Trident* but varied in superstructure design and carried different gear handling machinery.

*Silver Lining, renamed **Persevere** LH444 at anchor following her lengthening at Bideford Shipyard.*

Tests showed that she failed to comply with IMCO's minimum stability standards in certain conditions of loading. Modifications designed by a leading authority on fishing vessel stability, consultant naval architects The Napier Co. (Arbroath) Ltd., enabled her to satisfy the criteria and made her safe.

The work was carried out in 1976 at Bideford Shipyard in north Devon and involved lengthening her by 11ft 8in and making some alterations to her superstructure and fuel and water tanks.

The loss of *Trident* also drew attention to the importance of having freeing ports extended well forward to enable water to escape from below the whaleback if a vessel's bow was well down in a following sea, and so *Silver Lining* had these put in also.

In order to be lengthened, *Silver Lining* was cut in two through the after end of her fishroom. The two halves were pulled apart and the new midship section was built in.

The modifications gave her greater buoyancy so that her freeboard increased. Together with correct ballasting the alterations lowered her centre of gravity and increased the length of the 'GZ' righting lever where needed.

Renamed *Persevere* LH444 she spent a short time trawling for mackerel off Cornwall and for sprats from North Shields. Later she returned to white fish catching from Scottish ports.

Shipyard closures.

Peculiar things happened to more than a dozen boats under construction in British yards for Scottish skippers during the middle 1970s.

Rampant inflation and the general industrial recession threw several shipyards into disarray and forced them out of business leaving vessels only partly built.

Some of these were finally completed in other yards some three or four years after the original orders were placed and their owners faced heavy financial commitments as inflation pushed up the final costs.

Built twice.

One victim of shipyard closure was built twice.

Southern Shipbuilders (London) Ltd. of Faversham went into receivership when the Peterhead seiner trawler *Marigold* PD145 was under construction.

Bideford Shipyard won the contract to complete her but because the after end of the hull was still to be plated, and this work could not be done at Faversham, workmen from Bideford cut the boat into some twenty pieces for transport to Devon on a fleet of lorries.

Marigold was handed over to Skipper Peter Duncan in 1976, four years after he ordered her from Southern Shipbuilders. He was delighted with the work done at Bideford Shipyard which took twelve months to rebuild and complete her. When the hull was being re-assembled the welding was X-rayed to ensure that all was in order.

Bearing the same name as a steam drifter once owned by the Duncan family the cruiser sterned *Marigold* measured just short of 80ft with beam of 22ft. She was powered by a B & W Alpha air starting engine of 500hp at 400rpm coupled by direct drive to a controllable pitch propeller.

She carried an aluminium gutting shelter, which by 1976 had become a usual feature on Scottish seiners.

[1] Statutory Instrument 1975 No.330 *The Fishing Vessels (Safety Provisions) Rules 1975.*

[2] Inter Governmental Maritime Consultative Organisation *Recommendation on Intact Stability of Fishing Vessels.*

Marigold PD 45, the boat which was built twice.

Chapter 4
SAFETY, ECONOMY AND CONSERVATION

Skippers have lots of ideas.

Things began to recover from the cost and price crisis of 1974 and 1975.

Better catch rates and higher quayside prices lifted the value of fish landed by British vessels at Scottish ports from £59.3 million in 1975 to a colossal £85.8 million in 1976.

This showed a substantial rise of 45 per cent and, as the rate of inflation began to ease down, the boats enjoyed an increase in their real income.

About 190 boats in the 30ft to 79.9ft registered length category were built for Scotland during the years 1976 to 1981 inclusively. At the start of the 1970s the emphasis had been placed firmly on increasing the catching ability of boats and fishing gear but now owners and builders were looking at different ideas against a bewildering background of political and economic considerations. Conservation became vitally important because of declining catch rates in many parts of the world.

In order to reduce fishing effort and allow stocks to regenerate, catch limitations or 'quotas' for species under serious pressure were prescribed by international fisheries organisations.

Fishermen also went through the 1970s without knowing the final outcome of the European Community's Common Fisheries Policy renegotiation regarding in particular the future quota share-outs between member states and the access of Community boats to Britain's coastal waters and proposals for restructuring the fishing fleets.

Britain had entered the EC in 1973 and the Community extended its territorial limits to 200 miles in 1977, but a revised CFP was not formulated until 1983.

Meantime Britain exercised its rights under the Hague Agreement to impose several unilateral conservation measures including a total ban on herring fishing in the North Sea from 1977 until the early 1980s.

Heavy overheads coupled with catch quotas led the fishermen to look for ways of keeping costs down and also keeping fish in the best possible condition in order to attract high market prices.

Uncertainty over the outcome of the CFP caused many skippers and owners to want versatile boats which could fish with maximum profitability for a variety of species within EC waters and elsewhere.

Safety.

Safety of vessels and crews and improved standards of living and working conditions came very much to the forefront.

Drawn up in consultation with the fishing industry The Fishing Vessels (Safety Provisions) Rules 1975[1] laid down requirements in respect of stability and freeboard, hull strength, watertight integrity, machinery, electrical equipment, bilge pumping arrangements, fire protection and detection systems, steering gear, compasses, life saving appliances and other matters relating to the safety of fishermen and boats.

To be met by British vessels of 12m registered length and over, the Rules applied to new boats whose keels were laid on or after 1st May 1975 and to existing ones which were to be surveyed over a period of time and modified where necessary. Amendments were added to the Rules as thought necessary as time went by.

The Merchant Shipping (Radio) (Fishing vessels) Rules 1974 also came into operation in 1975, specifying radio equipment to be carried by fishing boats.

[1] Statutory Instrument 1975 No. 330 *The Fishing Vessels (Safety Provisions) Rules 1975.*

First 85 footer from Campbeltown.

Optimistic skipper.

Although fishing was going through a lean time in 1974 and 1975 there were some fishermen who felt that things would improve. Skipper William Campbell MBE, who by now had spent thirty-five years at sea, had seen even worse shortages of fish but the shoals had always returned.

He said 'Like the harvest on the land the fishing always seems to go in cycles, with lean years followed by better years'. In his opinion, he said, the current scarcity was Nature's way of conserving the stocks and forcing the fleet back to a more normal number of boats.

Skipper Campbell declared his trust in the future by having the 85ft seiner trawler *Ajax* INS168 built by Campbeltown Shipyard in 1975, as a more ample version of the 80ft sister ships *Ajax* and *Argosy* which came from the yard in 1972.

Since delivering these two, Campbeltown had built thirteen similar vessels of 75ft and 80ft for Scottish skippers.

With beam of 23.60ft and depth of 12ft she was the first of the Campbeltown 85ft vessels and proved herself to be as economical to operate as the 80 footers and her bigger carrying capacity gave her even more potential.

Extra space on deck and below provided better living and working conditions for her crew.

In response to the swingeing costs of the mid 1970s *Ajax* had several features aimed at economy and ease of maintenance.

Machinery was kept simple and such that any mechanical breakdown could be dealt with by her own engineer, thereby avoiding costly and time-consuming repairs by shore firms.

Ajax INS168 was the first 'Campbeltown 85'. Originally she had seine rope storage bins but was equipped with rope reels later. However, she kept the bins as they were useful when switching to different lengths of rope off the west coast.

Storage bins.

Skipper Campbell had even considered fitting a mechanically driven winch but later abandoned this idea. All her electrics were 24V, being simpler to maintain and safer to handle than the more powerful systems and everything could be run from the batteries if need be.

Seine rope storage bins were chosen in preference to hydraulically powered reels not only being maintenance-free but allowing *Ajax* to be dual purpose without delays ashore to fit out for different modes of fishing.

If she was herring trawling, but came across good white fish 'marks' for instance, the seine ropes would be ready in the bins and ready for use. In order that her Caterpillar 565hp engine could use all its power for propulsion when the fishing gear was being hauled, the winch was driven from a Dowty variable delivery hydraulic pump powered from the Gardner 115hp auxiliary engine.

Successful builder.

Ajax was the 23rd fishing vessel to be built by Campbeltown Shipyard since it began production in 1970. By now it employed 150 people and enjoyed some twenty-five per cent of the market for steel seiner trawlers in the 60ft to 90ft size range.

Ajax was the fifth vessel to go down its slipway in twenty-two weeks and was one of seven boats completed in 1975.

Less Hazardous.

In 1976 James Noble (Fraserburgh) Ltd. delivered the 65ft wooden hulled vessel *Fruitful Harvest III* PD247 to Skipper Robert Reid of Peterhead. At first sight she looked like a normal seiner but her skipper had given mindful attention to detail throughout the boat and many things were planned to make life less hazardous for the fishermen and to keep costs low.

Where possible, her fittings were chosen so that they could be maintained or set to rights by the crew.

Three rope reels.

A three-drum system of rope storage reels was designed to make gear handling less dangerous and to prolong rope life.

When hauling the seine net it was desirable to have the older ropes nearer the net where the strain was least and the newer ropes nearer the boat where the strain was greatest.

If only two reels were used, the first side of rope unavoidably got turned around each tow so that during every alternate haul the old rope was nearer the vessel and should it snap it could injure a crewman on deck. The newer rope was near the net and tended to stick in the mud. Reversing the rope also caused greater wear because it got rubbed both ways instead of always in the same direction.

Use of three reels eliminated these problems. After the gear had been hauled, the rope could be wound off one reel onto the spare one so that the correct end could be run out first every time. The second side of rope did not need turning since it was always set from the net first and stayed the correct way round.

There was also a spare reel for use should one break down, and *Fruitful Harvest III* carried no rope coiler.

The position of winch and reels and the run of the ropes were also carefully thought out in order to save deck room and reduce strain on ropes and guiding-on gear. From the winch the ropes ran forward around guides beneath the whaleback and back at a shallow angle onto the reels which were positioned athwartships rather than fore-aft. Consequently the ropes travelled round fewer corners.

The end flanges of the reels were an open-spoked design rather than steel plate, thereby reducing weight without loss of strength.

Controls for winch and reels were in the wheelhouse and therefore no-one need be on deck forward.

New winch.

The seine winch was the new Mastra Mk II from the Northern Tool and Gear Co. In place of bevel gears and an internal low speed high torque Dowmax hydraulic

*The three rope storage reels being fitted to **Fruitful Harvest III**
so that the ropes could be 'turned'.*

motor it had a high speed low torque Dowmatic motor mounted on the outside of the winch with worm and worm wheel drive.

This arrangement helped to protect the hydraulics, gave a better heave and prevented the barrels from running back, and the motor was more accessible for removal and maintenance.

Rope reels, landing winch, and 24in power block on a single reach crane were made by the Lossie Hydraulic Co. The midships rope leads, from A. F. Engineering of Peterhead, were of the greased pin type, being simpler and more rugged than the usual ball-bearing models. The bulwark was higher on the afterdeck to give the fishermen more safety when handling the net, and a window in the after end of the wheelhouse enabled the skipper to see the net being shot and hauled.

G. L. Watson.

With lines designed by G. L. Watson, *Fruitful Harvest III* had a hefty beam of 22ft and was quite full aft with wide transom stern, but fairly fine forward to improve speed and prevent her from thumping into the sea.

She was powered by a Gardner 8L3B engine of 230hp at 1150rpm turning a 64in diameter Bruntons propeller through a Twin Disc gearbox of 4.3:1 reduction ratio. This was relatively low power but supplied propulsion only since the Dowty winch pump and the Vickers pump for the other deck units were clutch driven from the Gardner 6LX 120hp auxiliary engine.

The lighter work load on the main engine, together with the bigger propeller and reduction ratio, gave about fifty per cent more towing power which was of particular value when the gear was being closed. Each engine drove a Gilbert Gilkes and Gordon GGG bilge and general

Fruitful Harvest III PD247 nearing completion in Fraserburgh.
Although she looked unremarkable she had a number of features which made gear handling safer for her crew.

service pump and an alternator, the electrics being 24V for simplicity. Fuel consumption was economical owing to rational use of the engines. By using the auxiliary to drive the deck machinery the main engine was not pushed too hard. A control in the wheelhouse enabled the smaller engine to be throttled down when its full power was not needed.

Wheelhouse layout was planned for safety and efficiency. The casing was lower than normal to give virtually all-round visibility from the large wheelhouse windows.

Electronic equipment included Kelvin Hughes Kingfisher II Fishfinding System, and Simrad SL Sonar for 'picking up the ground'.

Individual ideas.

Skipper John W. C. Thomson of Lossiemouth was deeply concerned about stability deficiencies diagnosed in some boats.

His 79.9ft cruiser sterned steel seiner trawler *St. Kilda* INS47, built by Herd and Mackenzie in 1978, was designed to have stability features well in excess of statutory requirements.

With moulded beam of 23.70ft and moulded depth of 13.50ft she was deep and beamy with full lines and her superstructure was of low profile to reduce top weight.

Positioning of fuel and water tanks was also a good stability feature. A total of 4,600 gallons of fuel were carried in the double bottom below the fishroom and in wing tanks in the engineroom, and a thousand gallons of fresh water in the double bottom beneath the fishroom, thereby keeping weights low down. A salt water ballast tank below the net store forward could be filled and emptied by the main bilge pumps.

Her scantlings were well above Lloyds minimum requirements and steel was chosen to provide a strong versatile boat suitable for the possible future development of white fish trawling techniques.

She was powered by a Caterpillar 720hp engine with fixed pitch propeller and 4.6:1 reduction gear.

Skipper Thomson said 'Herd and Mackenzie have allowed me to be as individual as I can be in trying to evolve the most efficient craft. In her hull form and design I think she is very advanced in the interests of seaworthiness'.

To fit her for working seine net gear off the Scottish west coast *St. Kilda* carried Fishing Hydraulics rope reels

St. Kilda INS47 sets out for her trials. She was deep and beamy with full lines. Note her rope reels which had additional flanges.

of new design. The nature of the ground often made it necessary to set the net in restricted areas and use less warp.

The design of the reels enabled the desired number of coils to be used for each fishing cycle. Each reel could hold thirteen coils of 3½in rope on its main drum, but had a smaller drum onto which unwanted rope could be wound.

Renewed interest in reels.

From the mid 1970s onwards there was a renewed interest in reels in preference to storage bins. Ropes were found to suffer tremendous wear when leaving the bins and as a crewman needed to stand near the bins when the gear was being set he was in danger of being dragged overboard by fouled rope. Bins also took up valuable fishroom space.

Reels could be controlled from the wheelhouse so that no-one need be near them during rope shooting and hauling. Ropes suffered less damage and the fishing cycle could be speeded up and the skipper had more precise control over shooting the ropes. Most new seiners fitted reels and there was a steady stream of conversions on existing vessels from bins to reels.

The bulk of the market was shared by Fishing Hydraulics (Scotland) Ltd. and the Lossie Hydraulic Co. Ltd., and sets of reels awaiting installation became a regular quayside sight.

A two-drum set from Fishing Hydraulics was supplied to Skipper Willie Campbell's 85ft *Ajax*.

No hesitation.

Skipper David Smith MBE had no hesitation in fitting reels to his new 80ft steel seiner *Argonaut IV* KY157 built by Campbeltown Shipyard in 1976.

Skipper Smith had done remarkably well with his

*In 1978 **Argonaut IV** KY157 was the second highest earning white fish boat in Britain, with a grossing of £480,000.*

wooden hulled *Argonaut III* and put up an even more splendid performance with *Argonaut IV*. In 1978 she was the second highest earning white fish boat in Britain. Her grossing of £480,000 was outstripped only by the 185ft distant water stern trawler *C S Forester*.

Arranged for seine netting only, *Argonaut IV* was the fifteenth 80 footer from Campbeltown and was similar to the earlier boats in shape and dimensions, but her lines were slightly filled out aft to provide roomier accommodation below deck.

Her fittings were of more powerful or advanced design than those on *Argonaut III*.

A 24RA 2300 power block was hung from a Hiab 550 Speedloader crane.

Developed initially for use on trucks for moving and handling goods, these articulated cranes were strong and manoeuvrable and ideal for working a power block and the *Argonaut IV* installation was the first of many in the fishing fleet.

Mounted on her afterdeck it could rotate on its own axis and had an outreach of some 11ft, and the block could be worked above and below deck level.

Block and crane were supplied by Fishing Hydraulics which also made the two rope reels which held fifteen coils of 3in rope and had open-spoked flanges. A Beccles coiler was fitted for standby use.

Fishing Hydraulics had introduced its open spoked design in 1975 when it provided two reels to the 86ft *Inter Nos* A477, built by John Lewis and Sons.

Argonaut IV had a new echosounder from Elac, the LAZ72 recording sounder. Smaller yet more efficient than earlier Elac models it used solid state electronics and a ceramic transducer.

Recordings could be made on the 9in wide paper of the LAZ72 in a choice of fifteen range scales, and clear detection of fish near the seabed could be achieved with the grey line system.

Her second fishfinder was a Furuno Universal Graph recording sounder. Most boats were fitting two echosounders by this time. *Argonaut IV* was powered by a Caterpillar D379TA engine of 565hp at 1225rpm.

It drove a Bruntons propeller through a 3.95:1 reduction gearbox. The Dowty pump for the winch and Vickers double pump for rope reels and power block were operated from the Gardner 6LXB auxiliary engine.

On deck a Mastra Mk II seine winch from the Northern Tool and Gear Co. was sited well forward and was in fact the first of these new units to enter service having been in use for a short time on *Argonaut III* before being transferred to the new boat.

Fishroom cooling plants.

In addition to reducing their operating expenses in the 1970s the fishermen were looking for ways of landing their catches in good condition in order to attract high market prices.

Fishroom cooling systems could preserve quality by keeping fish temperature at just above freezing point and preventing the ice supply from melting away too quickly.

Skipper Eric Smith of Buckie recognised the advantages of a cooling plant when he had one fitted to his new 74ft seiner trawler *Rhodella* BCK100, built in 1977 by Jones Buckie Shipyard.

He said that without such equipment a ten ton supply of ice could melt away well before the end of a five or six day trip and cause severe problems, as had happened during the hot summers of 1975 and 1976.

Rhodella's cooling system came from Currie and Thomson (Engineers) Ltd. which had already supplied earlier versions of the equipment to several wooden hulled seiners.

The equipment aboard *Rhodella* was designed to chill the after half of the fishroom and incorporated a 3hp water cooled Frigidaire compressor fitted in the forecastle and driven from the 110V electricity supply. It fed four tube evaporators fitted on the deckhead in the after section of fishroom.

Insulated on deckhead and both bulkheads with high density slab polystyrene with timber cladding, the

***Rhodella** BCK100 was a typical example of a wooden hulled transom sterned seiner trawler built in the latter half of the 1970s, but was among the first to have a fishroom cooling plant.*

fishroom was fitted with aluminium stanchions and wooden pound boards and was served by a single hatch.

Once the cooling plant was in operation the fishroom could be kept at a predetermined temperature even if the trip was prolonged because of bad weather or fish shortage.

During the late 1970s fishroom cooling plants were arousing a great deal of interest among the fishermen and a few new and existing seiners and white fish trawlers were fitted with them.

Late in 1977 *Argonaut IV* became the first Scottish seiner to be fitted with a cooling system from Promac of

Holland. Skipper David Smith believed that it would become even more imperative to land catches in top condition as fish became scarcer.

Argonaut IV's cooling plant used sixteen evaporators which kept fishroom temperature at 2 degrees C and the compressor was driven from the 110V electricity supply.

Smart and pleasing.

Built to G. L. Watson lines the transom sterned wooden hulled *Rhodella* was of smart and pleasing appearance with very fair lines. With a beam of 21ft 6in she was constructed throughout to comply with the Fishing Vessels (Safety Provisions) Rules 1975.

She was the second *Rhodella* to be built by Jones for Skipper Smith, the first, BCK110, having been a very pretty 71ft cruiser sterned vessel completed in 1966 and powered by a Gardner 200hp engine.

Skipper Smith chose a transom stern for the new *Rhodella* as it gave more space above and below deck and other skippers assured him that it did not impair a boat's seakeeping abilities.

Apart from having the cooling plant which was still a somewhat uncommon feature in 1977 *Rhodella* typified the medium sized wooden hulled seiners being built by Scottish yards in the middle years of the 1970s.

Fittings included Kelvin 500hp engine with 4:1 reduction gear, Sutherland seine and trawl winch, Lossie Hydraulics rope reels and power block, Elac echosounders, and aluminium gutting shelter.

Some skippers prefer cruiser sterns.

The number of wooden and steel transom sterned boats in the 50ft to 86ft size range built during the first six or seven years of the 1970s outnumbered those with cruiser sterns by almost two to one. But the cruiser stern was still preferred by many seine net skippers as its rounded shape provided a smooth and continuous support for the ropes whereas other skippers felt that it gave a boat superior handling qualities.

Almost all the cruiser sterned steel boats came from

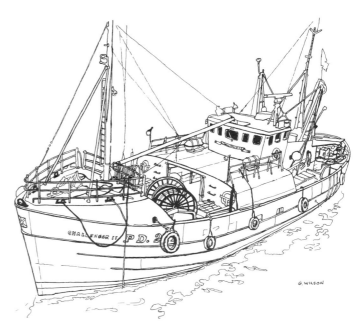

Challenger II PD212 was the third 85-footer from Campbeltown Shipyard. Built in 1977 for Skipper Andrew Strachan she was powered by a Mirrlees Blackstone 600hp engine and carried Lossie Hydraulics gear handling machinery and Elac echosounder. Skipper Strachan said she handled well during very stormy weather.

Campbeltown Shipyard which by the close of 1977 had supplied twenty-one in the 75ft, 80ft and 85ft class to Scottish skippers.

Among builders of wooden hulled vessels Richard Irvin at Peterhead never built a transom sterned boat and was to complete its final vessel the 85ft *Sunbeam* INS189 in 1978. During the 1970s it built thirteen cruiser sterned boats almost all in the 80ft size range. *Sunbeam* was the 102nd boat to come from Irvins since it started work in 1914.

Other cruiser sterned wooden hulled boats included the 74ft seiner trawler *Aeolus* BCK143, built in 1977 by Macduff Boatbuilding and Engineering Co. for Skipper George Findlay of Buckie. Named after the God of the

The 85ft cruiser sterned seiner trawler **Sunbeam** *INS189 under construction. She was the last boat built by Richard Irvin and Sons. Note her double oak frames.*
She was owned by successful seine net skipper William Smith of Lossiemouth.

Aeolus BCK143 coming into Peterhead with a very big catch of white fish. Built at Macduff in 1977 for Skipper George Findlay of Buckie she had a cruiser stern.

Sarepta FR207 was one of the largest wooden hulled cruiser sterned boats built in the late 1970s. Unlike many vessels built at that time she had no gutting shelter. The photograph shows her beautiful lines to advantage. Note her controllable pitch propeller and the cantilever-type trawl gallows.

75

Adelphi KY147 presented a new concept in deckhouse design.
Her wheelhouse was set on the after end of the casing
rather than in the usual place on the forward end.

Winds in Greek mythology *Aeolus* was about the 60th Scottish built wooden vessel designed by G. L. Watson since 1963.

One of the largest wooden cruiser sterners from this time came from J. and G. Forbes. She was the 86ft x 23ft seiner trawler *Sarepta* FR207, built in 1976 for Skipper John Noble of Fraserburgh and powered by an 850hp Caterpillar engine with controllable pitch propeller.

Sarepta had rope bins and no gutting shelter, whereas *Aeolus* had rope reels and an aluminium shelter.

Outside the general run of things.

There are fishermen who will stand aside from the general run of things and try out new ideas.

There was an intriguing variation in deck layout aboard the 74ft steel seiner trawler *Adelphi* KY147, built in 1976 for Skipper Peter Murray of Anstruther.

Her wheelhouse was set on the after end of her casing rather than in the usual position on the forward end. This location gave the skipper a complete view of the afterdeck where most of the work went on, but also enabled him to see forward to the rope reels and winch.

He also had a full view of the cod end being lifted up for emptying into the deck pounds because the gilson blocks were hung from a goalpost-type derrick mounted on the casing top just forward of the wheelhouse.

Adelphi was dual purpose in that she could go to sea ready for working seines or trawls as desired. For working the trawl a net drum was positioned on the afterdeck in line with a small stern ramp, and towing posts were sited at the quarters.

She was powered by a Caterpillar 425hp engine, and the exhaust funnels emerged on the casing top forward of the wheelhouse.

Adelphi was the product of two yards. She was designed and fitted out by James N. Miller and Sons Ltd. of St. Monans, and her hull and basic superstructure built by McTay Marine Ltd. on Merseyside.

In steel boatbuilding during the 1970s there was a trend towards one yard building hulls and another fitting them out. Hulls were constructed by firms skilled in steel shipbuilding techniques and the vessels completed in Scotland by well established builders of wooden boats.

The shelterdeck and new ideas in layout; a foretaste.

Gutting shelters were by now in general use in the seiner trawler fleet. Normally these structures were arranged around the forward part of the casing and extended forward to the fishroom hatch.

A noteworthy little vessel built in 1977 took the concept a step further and gave a foretaste of the three-quarter length shelters which were to have a big impact on gear and catch handling methods and provide the fishermen with a safer and more comfortable working environment.

She was the 54ft wooden hulled seiner trawler *Orion* KY352 built by Gerrard Brothers at Arbroath for Skipper William Scott of St. Monans and her shelter continued forward along the port side to join up with the whaleback. The starboard section remained conventional with a bulkhead at its forward end and an open area between it and the whaleback.

Made of aluminium the shelter gave protection to the crewmen and also formed a cover for the Skovgaard Speedwinch rope reel assembly fitted to port on the foredeck. *Orion* was among the first Scottish boats to fit this Danish unit which enabled the ropes to be turned. This was done by winding the ropes from the smaller reel onto the larger, after which both sides of rope could be set from the larger reel.

Although power blocks and rope reels had brought a good degree of automation to seine netting there had been little change in the placing of gear handling machinery on board the conventional seine netter.

With the winch position forward the ropes were hauled in along the deck where they could be inconvenient and dangerous for the men busy gutting the catch.

A radical departure from this layout was made by Skipper Ian Sutherland of Hopeman when he had the 85ft cruiser sterned steel boat *Kestrel* INS253 built by Campbeltown Shipyard in 1978.

Her seine net winch and rope reels were fitted on the after deck so that the fishing gear could be worked from the stern thereby keeping the ropes well away from the catch handling area forward of the deckhouse.

This arrangement also enabled *Kestrel* to have a

*Port view of **Orion** KY352 showing her shelterdeck extending from wheelhouse to whaleback. The rather awkward lines of the shelter result from it not being specified at the design stage.*

Kestrel INS253 had winch and rope reels aft and a three-quarter-length shelterdeck.

shelterdeck extending from abaft the wheelhouse right forward to the stem so giving the crewmen protection from the weather.

The shelter differed from that fitted to *Orion* in that it was not open at the starboard side forward and was in fact the first true shelterdeck which feature was to so strongly alter the appearance of the Scottish seiner trawler in the 1980s.

Over the top.

Some skippers looked for other ways of keeping ropes clear of the main deck.

Campbeltown Shipyard's sixth 85 footer *Resplendent* PD298, built in 1979 for one of Scotland's most skilful seine net skippers David John Forman of Peterhead, was one of several seiners arranged to shoot ropes over the gutting shelter.

They travelled aft from the reels via rollers fitted on the shelter top and on the outrigger-type trawl gallows. In order to produce a good looking boat the profile of *Resplendent*'s superstructure was more streamlined and her stem had a slightly greater rake than earlier Campbeltown vessels.

Aesthetic considerations were also applied to the 67.8ft cruiser sterned wooden hulled seiner trawler *Kevella* BF364 built by Macduff Boat Building in 1980 for Skipper James Johnston of Macduff. The top of her gutting shelter was shaped to harmonise with the line of her toprail so avoiding the box-like appearance of many shelters.

Kevella set her ropes via rollers on the shelter top and a block hung from the gallows.

Each of *Kevella*'s rope reels was designed to hold 24 coils of rope. Many seiners were fitting these larger reels

Resplendent PD298 set her seine ropes over her shelter through rollers fitted on the shelter and on top of the canti-lever type trawl gallows. Note the net drum at the stern.

Kevella BF364 leaving Macduff for acceptance trials. Her gutting shelter was shaped to give a pleasing appearance.

as they enabled both fleets of rope to be run onto one reel to reach rope near the core of the opposite reel for repair. They could also be used to haul the second fleet of ropes onto the full reel when retrieving damaged fishing gear.

Resplendent and *Kevella*'s seine rope towing rollers, for mounting on the stern rail, came from Lockwood Torday and Carlisle Ltd. of North Shields.

The rollers were developed following consultation with two leading North Shields skippers Norrie Morse and Alan Morse Jnr. Exhaustive sea trials with the prototype on their boats *Conduan BCK4 and Congener* BCK128 showed that they could outlast conventional rollers by several working lives.

Seamless rustproof armour used on the rollers extended the life of rollers and ropes. The strength of the frame had been proved to beyond the maximum towing load for vessels of 850hp and the whole assembly was light enough to be picked up by one man. All four rollers were reversible and opposite pairs interchangeable to even out excessive wear on any one roller. Bearings were triple sealed against sand and seawater and the frame was mounted on a high tensile steel swivel pin.

Accurate weight distribution gave the equipment a quick and responsive steer.

Offset to port.

Other new ideas in deck and superstructure layout were explored. In 1978 J. and G. Forbes built the 74ft wooden hulled white fish trawler *Constellation II* FR295 for Skipper Joe Buchan. The casing containing galley and messdeck was offset to port and a deck shelter extended to the starboard rail while the wheelhouse was set on the centreline above casing and shelter.

A net drum was positioned below the shelter so providing ample space abaft the drum for the heavy bobbin gear when the demersal trawl had been hauled. *Constellation II* worked her gear from the stern, the net being hauled through an opening in the transom bulwark in line with the drum.

The power block was used to take the cod end around to the starboard side where it was lifted aboard by the gilson derrick and emptied into the deck pounds forward. Conventional A-frame gallows were fitted on the quarters.

The port warp travelled forward inside the port rail to the winch while the starboard one passed through the deck shelter space.

Further developments in the shelterdeck.

There was further development of the three-quarter length shelterdeck. Macduff Boatbuilding made a substantial early start with shelterdeckers in 1979, one being the 65ft transom sterned wooden hulled *Fortitude* BF305 for Skipper David Lovie of Whitehills.

During trawling the cod end was taken aboard through a hatch in the starboard side of the shelter. Seine catches were lifted aboard at the quarters in the traditional manner.

Ropes were payed out through small openings in the shelter top.

Weathertight.

Another shelterdecker was the 74ft transom sterned wooden hulled white fish trawler *Steadfast II* FR443 delivered from J. and G. Forbes to Skipper Sandy West of Fraserburgh in 1980.

Her shelter differed from that of *Fortitude* in that it was classed as 'weathertight' when all its openings were closed. In the seiner trawler fleet, shelterdecks, which were of steel or aluminium, were now evolving into two main types, namely weathertight or non-weathertight.

Weathertight, in relation to structures and fittings in fishing vessel construction means that 'in any sea conditions water will not penetrate into the vessel'.[2]

Weathertight shelterdecks therefore prevented the ingress of water when all doors and hatches were closed, and the main openings had shutters fitted with rubber seals and special locking devices. Pumps extracted water which collected on the main deck from the fish handling process or happened to get in when the hatches and doors were open.

[2] IMCO *Recommendation on Intact Stability of Fishing Vessels* Supplement 1972.

Fortitude BF305 was the second boat built at Macduff with a three-quarter-length shelterdeck. The bag hatch was set in the starboard side of the shelter forward of the wheelhouse.

Steadfast II FR443 coming into Fraserburgh after her sea trials. Her shelterdeck was classed as 'weathertight' when all its openings were closed.

The cod-end hatch, more usually called the 'bag hatch', was normally in the shelter top, and the sills of doors in the after end of the shelter were a specified minimum height.

Weathertight shelters were of stouter construction, and the bulwark planks of wooden hulled boats were heavier and caulked weathertight.

Such shelters were taken into account when assessing stability in that the enclosed area was regarded as being a large buoyancy tank and the shelter sides were considered as additional freeboard.

Extra haul upwards.

Although the shelter could have adverse effects on stability at small angles of heel because of the additional top weight, this could be offset by the use of ballast. But at large angles of heel the extra freeboard was advantageous, extending the length of the GZ righting lever, and the buoyancy tank effect helped to bring the boat upright.

Weathertight shelters could greatly enhance a vessel's stability characteristics and bring her well above the minimum requirements. However, such shelters were expensive and the position of the bag hatch necessitated an extra haul upwards for the cod end.

Non-weathertight shelters often had weathertight shutters or doors for their various openings. Bag hatches were normally set into the shelter side to enable the cod end to be simply lifted over the bulwark, but they should close weathertight.

The hatch should open into an open space provided with drainage such as scuppers leading directly overboard.

These types of shelter did not constitute additional freeboard or buoyancy tanks for stability calculations, but in accordance with the statutory regulations the boats would satisfy the stability criteria.

Around 1980 there was a transitional period in the design of the two types of shelter. *Steadfast II* was one of a handful of weathertight shelterdeckers to have a bag hatch set into the side of the shelter, the regulation asking for the hatch to be in the top not coming into effect until 1983.

Cooling.

Seacool Ltd. of Peterhead supplied *Steadfast II*'s fishroom cooling plant. An electric motor in the engineroom powered the compressor which served sixteen finned coil evaporators mounted on the fishroom deckhead.

After a year's fishing with *Steadfast II* Skipper West told Seacool that the equipment enabled him to use two or three tons of ice less per trip and receive better prices for his catches. *Steadfast II* was designed to stay at sea longer in order to cut down on the number of runs to and from port and save fuel. With a fishroom capacity for 900 boxes she could land two weeks' quotas at a time.

Fish tanks.

Whereas fishroom cooling plants were playing an increasing role in the white fish fleet, pursers and herring pair trawlers were using chilled seawater (CSW) tanks and refrigerated seawater (RSW) tanks.

With RSW tanks a mechanical refrigeration plant with a heat exchanger is used to maintain the storage temperature at just above the freezing point of the fish.

Tanks are ideal for handling and stowing herring and mackerel which are caught in large numbers over a short period.

In 1978 the Shetland purser *Zephyr* LK319 and the Fraserburgh pair trawlers *Sarepta* FR207 and *Qui Vive* FR201 were the first wooden hulled boats to be fitted with tanks. *Zephyr* was given CSW tanks whereas the others had RSW systems.

During the following year the 86ft transom sterned 840hp seiner trawler *Scottish Maid* BF317 was the first wooden hulled boat to be fitted with tanks at the time of her building. Made by Kvaerner Kulde a/s of Norway

Scottish Maid BF317 was the first wooden hulled boat in Scotland to be fitted with RSW tanks at the time of her building.

the refrigeration plant was designed to cool 26 tonnes of seawater from fifteen to 0 degrees C in four hours.

A Volvo 80hp engine drove the compressor and also the two pumps for the condenser and for circulating seawater through cooler and tanks.

Low fuel consumption.

Built by J. and G. Forbes for Skipper John Scott of Gardenstown *Scottish Maid* was the first boat built in Scotland to have a Hedemora engine and Berg controllable pitch propeller. Skipper Scott chose the

Golden Sceptre BF354 coming into Fraserburgh after her acceptance trials. Note the hatches over her RSW tanks, and the layout of her superstructure.

Honeybourne II BF359 leaving Macduff for trials. Her bag hatch was set into the starboard side of her shelter with the gilson derrick above. Her power block was set to starboard of the net drum at the stern.

*Built in 1958 for seine net skipper John Leask the 75ft **Fear Not** A249 was one of a series of cruiser sterned wooden hulled boats from Richard Irvin and Sons Ltd. at Peterhead. The majority varied slightly from one another in hull form.*

*The 80ft steel seiner trawler **Starwood** A353 was built in 1981 by John Wood Group Ship Repairing Ltd., formerly John Lewis and Sons, for Skipper John Stewart. The three-quarter-length shelterdeck was just coming into general use, and **Starwood's** shelter had rather awkward lines because it was not asked for at the design stage.*

There has been a long association between Scottish boatbuilders and the English port of Whitby. James N. Miller and Sons Ltd. of St. Monans built the 60ft steel trawler **Sophie Louise** *WY168 for Skipper Howard Locker in 1988.*

Andrianne *INS8 is one of the newest wooden hulled boats in Scotland. Built in 1992 by Macduff Shipyards Ltd. for Skipper Sandy Patience she has full length shelterdeck and was designed to fish in deep water off the Scottish west coast.*
Photograph courtesy Macduff Shipyards Ltd.

engine for its relatively low fuel consumption.

More wooden boats were built with RSW tanks. One such was the 74ft *Golden Sceptre* BF354 built by Forbes for Skipper George West of Peterhead in 1980. Her three tanks used a Lemkuhl chilling plant and held 40 tons of fish and seawater.

Her casing was offset to port and deck shelter extended to the starboard rail and continued forward to span the deck forward of the casing.

Golden Sceptre joined the growing number of boats to have a Deutz propulsion engine, in this instance an SBA 12M 816R of 660hp with Berg controllable pitch propeller and 4:1 reduction ratio.

Honeybourne II, a move towards greater beam and depth and fullness of line.

There was in the early 1980s a further move towards greater beam and depth and fullness of line.

This general all-round increase in the volume of the hull, together with a high freeboard, was a good stability feature and helped to balance the extra top weight of shelterdecks, bigger deckhouses, heavier deck machinery and the growing number of electronic instruments.

It also gave the fishermen more spacious and comfortable living and working conditions and enabled vessels to stay at sea longer and carry bigger catches.

From 1980 onwards some boats had a chunkiness which made vessels such as *Forthright* and *Achilles* for example, built in the late 1960s, appear slight of form. This was at variance with the impression of extreme stoutness which they themselves had given when new.

The 70ft wooden hulled transom sterned demersal and pelagic trawler *Honeybourne II* BF359 built by Macduff Boatbuilding in 1980 was full bodied.

She is described here in some detail as she serves to illustrate the developments reached by the start of the 1980s.

She was designed by the Napier Co. in association with the builders and her skipper George Wiseman of Gardenstown.

Although only 69.55ft long overall she had a hefty beam of 22.5ft and depth from underside of keel to top of deck beam of 13.1ft. Compared with *Forthright* she was of fuller form and beamier and deeper with fuller bilges and flatter floors and her beam was continued for a greater part of her length.

Honeybourne II's three-quarter-length aluminium non-weathertight shelterdeck had a bag hatch with weathertight hinged shutters set into the starboard side amidships, and weathertight doors at the after end. A big strong gilson derrick of A-frame type was positioned on the shelter above the bag hatch. Gutting ports with sliding shutters were fitted along the shelter sides.

Her three-drum Jensen trawl winch was mounted athwartships forward, and the afterdeck housed Lossie Hydraulics net drum, and power block with articulated crane.

Warp tension meters from P. J. Products of Jarrow on Tyne were carried. The cylinders containing the load cells were carried on the casing top and linked to the warps. The meters gave early warning of the gear becoming fast and indicated when the net was full.

Other deck fittings included Lossie Hydraulics boom swinger and landing winch, Karmoy combined topping lift and windlass and A-frame trawl gallows.

The Turner Refrigeration fishroom cooling plant comprised an electrically driven compressor in the forepeak and four deckhead cooling coils in the after part of the fishroom. Insulated on the bulkheads and the after section of deckhead the fishroom had aluminium stanchions and wooden pound boards.

Honeybourne II was powered by a Kelvin TBSC8 engine of 495hp at 1315rpm driving the Bruntons fixed pitch propeller through a Reintjes gearbox of 4:1 reduction ratio. She carried 3,500 gallons of fuel oil and 700 of fresh water.

A Norgear single input multi output gearbox at the fore end of the engine provided belt drive for a Transmotor 110V generator, Transmotor 24V alternator and the steering gear pump, and direct drives for the

Dowty variable delivery hydraulic pump for the trawl winch and the Vickers pump for the other deck machinery. A Gilbert Gilkes and Gordon bilge and general service pump was belt driven from the gearbox input shaft. Macduff had already installed these robust gearboxes to several boats including *Kevella* and *Fortitude*. They were designed to provide all the auxiliary drives normally required on boats up to 100ft or so. Henry Fleetwood and Sons (Marine) Ltd. supplied the auxiliary generating set which was based on a Gardner 6LXB engine of 127hp. Another Dowty winch pump and Vickers pumps for the other deck units were driven from the forward end through a Twin Disc clutch.

A Transmotor 110V generator, Transmotor 24V alternator and a GGG bilge and general service pump were powered from the other end.

The wheelhouse was aluminium, and casing, masts and spars steel.

Colour echosounder.

Electronic instruments were largely from Marconi International Marine including Koden SRM872AV1 fishfinder with CRT display, NM850AT, Net Monitor, Chromascope CVS-887 Mk2 colour echosounder, Wesmar SS165 sonar, Sailor T126 R105 SSB radiotelephone, two Sailor RT144B VHF radiotelephones, Warden 4 watchkeeping receiver and Koden MD306 radar.

The net monitor showed the position of headline and footrope relative to the seabed and surface and registered the quantity of fish in the net. The Chromascope sounder displayed echoes in sixteen colours on a TV type screen in accordance with the echo density. For example, dense fish shoals showed as red to orange and sparse shoals as yellow through dark and light green to white. The Wesmar sonar scanned the seabed ahead and to the side of the boat during bottom trawling, enabling her to drag the net close to obstructions where fish tend to congregate.

For pelagic trawling it located fish at longer ranges and indicated scattered shoals.

Equipment from Racal Decca comprised Mk 21 Navigator, 350T Track Plotter, 150 radar, 450 automatic pilot and a Barkway intercom system.

Other fittings in the wheelhouse included Seafarer log, Wynstruments Mk3 window wiper, Fiamm horn, E Vejvad Hansen chair and Morse engine controls. Tenfjord 100 steering gear was coupled to the autopilot, and a hand held Francis searchlight was carried. A Falcon gas cooker and a gas geyser were fitted in the galley abaft the wheelhouse, and a berth for the skipper was arranged below the wheelhouse.

Eight bunks were fitted in the cabin which was heated by a gas fire. Safety equipment included a Tecaid fire detection and alarm system, Marinex bilge water level alarm, and a Gondolastic Gas Sentry.

Chalmit rubber cased floodlights were fitted on the superstructure. Domestic facilities included a shower, lavatory and washbasin in the casing.

Freeboard.

Safety factors continued to have paramount importance. The Fishing Vessel Safety Group had been set up in 1977 by the Dept. of Trade to advise upon implementation of the Fishing Vessels (Safety Provisions) Rules 1975. The group regularly considered and made recommendations on a variety of matters relating to safety, and amendments to the 1975 Rules were introduced as thought appropriate.

An amendment introduced in 1981 required vessels to have a specified minimum freeboard in all conditions of loading. The ruling was back-dated to include existing boats built under the 1975 Rules and the majority were found to comply.

The trawler *Quiet Waters III* FR353 built in 1981 was among the first to have the freeboard ruling taken into account at her design stage.

She was built by Macduff Boatbuilding for Skipper Albert Ritchie of Inverallochy.

Her lines were similar to those of *Honeybourne II*, but she was slightly bulkier, being a chunky looking craft

Steadfast III KY170 was the first fishing boat built by McCrindle Shipbuilding Ltd. of Ardrossan. She was handed over to skipper Alec Gardner in 1987. Her cruiser stern was more pointed than that on many steel vessels and she had quite a pronounced sheer.
Photograph courtesy William McCrindle and Son Ltd.

The rugged and full-bodied 75ft steel trawler *Westro* INS20 was delivered from Macduff Shipyards to Skipper Graham Thomson of Lossiemouth in 1992. She has a massive beam of 25ft and is capable of working the Atlantic deep water fisheries.
Photograph courtesy Macduff Shipyards Ltd.

*Richard Dunston (Hessle) Ltd. built the 86ft fully shelterdecked steel trawler **Veracious II** PD373 in 1988 for Skipper John Forman of Peterhead. She was primarily equipped for single and pair trawling but could switch to seine net fishing if required.*
Photograph courtesy Richard Dunston (Hessle) Ltd.

*James N. Miller and Sons delivered the 87ft steel seiner trawler **Carvida** FR457 to Skipper Andrew Buchan in 1988. Nets were worked through hatches in the transom.*
Photograph courtesy Judith Palmer.

Quiet Waters III FR353
was slightly beamier and chunkier
than Honeybourne II.

with overall length of 75ft, beam of 23ft and depth of 13.7ft and a fairly flared bow. Designed by Napier in association with builders and skipper *Quiet Waters III* had RSW tanks and three-quarter-length non-weathertight aluminium shelterdeck.

Her steel casing was offset to port and aluminium wheelhouse on the centreline, and a door in the casing gave access into the shelter-deck space. An A-frame gilson derrick was fitted above the bag hatch in the starboard side of the shelter just forward of the wheelhouse, for use in conjunction with one of the gilson winches for lifting cod ends aboard when the boat was catching white fish.

During pelagic fishing the hatch was closed by hinged and sliding shutters and a Rapp fish pump with fish and water separator was used to direct the catch into the RSW tanks via a small hatch in the shelter top.

Able to carry some 50 tons of fish and seawater the three insulated tanks were served by a Bolsones refrigeration plant in the forepeak. During white fish catching the tanks were used as dry fishroom space for carrying the catch in boxes and there was an additional short fishroom forward of the tanks.

Offloading hatches for pelagic and demersal catches were fitted in the shelterdeck.

Quiet Waters III was the second Scottish built boat to have a Hedemora engine, in this instance a V6A electric starting unit rated at 540hp at 1000 rpm and coupled to an Ulstein controllable pitch propeller through an Ulstein gearbox of 3.04:1 reduction ratio.

Variations.

There were variations in shelterdeck design.

The 74ft *Ardency* INS262, built in 1980 by Jones Buckie Shipyard for Skipper Norman Stewart was arranged to shoot her seine ropes from beneath her non-weathertight shelter using rollers on the deckhead.

Skipper William McPherson's 74ft *Fair Morn* INS308 built by Forbes in 1981 had a weathertight shelter. Ropes travelled out via openings in the shelter top. Both boats lifted the cod ends aboard at the quarters.

Ardency INS262 was unusual in being powered by twin Gardner 230hp engines turning a single propeller. Skipper Norman Stewart wanted Gardner power and chose the twin installation to provide the necessary horsepower of 460. Note her shelterdeck and articulated power block crane.

Fair Morn INS308 built in 1981 had a weathertight shelter. Seine ropes were payed out through cowls in the shelter top. J. and G. Forbes started building the boat 'on spec' at a time when there were few orders, but she was acquired by Skipper William McPherson of Forres.

Built in 1990 by J. and G. Forbes and Co. for Skipper John Nicol of Gardenstown the wooden hulled seiner trawler *Fruitful Vine* BF240 had a full length shelterdeck.
Photograph courtesy William McDonald.

The 65ft wooden hulled seiner *Hope* BCK59 was built by Herd and Mackenzie in 1986 for Skipper Gordon McKay. Her shelterdeck extended well aft to afford some shelter on the after deck without obstructing her skipper's view of net handling.
Photograph courtesy Judith Palmer.

Eleanda BCK60, now renamed **Kevella** BF364, built by Herd and Mackenzie in 1988 for Skipper David Main, was the first wooden hulled boat designed and constructed with a full length shelterdeck.

Skipper Alan Phimister's 77ft trawler *Faithful* UL179 was the first steel boat built by Jones Buckie Shipyard Ltd. Note the stout trawl gallows which also contain the engine exhausts.
Photograph courtesy
Jones Buckie Shipyard Ltd.

95

Jasper II PD174 was built to comply with new regulations
which were to have a tremendous influence on the development of boats
of less than 16.5 metres registered length.

John Wood Group Ship Repairing Ltd. (formerly John Lewis and Sons) produced the 80ft steel seiner trawler *Starwood* A353 in 1981 for Skipper John Stewart. The rather awkward lines of her non-weathertight shelter resulted from it not being specified at the design stage.

She was arranged to work one fishing method at a time to keep deck layout simple, but part of her shelter could be unbolted to permit changeover of deck units. Seine ropes travelled out through slots in the shelter.

All three had TV cameras below the shelter and screens in the wheelhouse to give the skipper a view of winch and rope reels.

Tremendous influence on design.

Although at first glance the 60ft transom sterned wooden hulled trawler *Jasper II* PD174, built in 1981 by James Noble, looked unremarkable she was most probably the first boat designed and built in compliance with new regulations which were to have far reaching implications for the future development of smaller vessels.

Having come into effect in 1980 the Merchant Shipping (United Kingdom Fishing Vessels: Manning) Regulation 1980 stipulated that boats with a registered length of less than 16.5m (54ft) were not required to carry a Certificated skipper. This ruling formerly applied to boats with a Gross Tonnage under Scottish Part IV Registry of less than 25.

Part IV Tonnage was a calculation based on length and beam and internal depth. Boats under 25 were thereby restricted in their beam and depth in proportion to their length.

As registered length was measured from the fore side of the rudder stock to the foremost side of the stem the new regulation enabled designers and builders to produce much more substantial beamier deeper full bodied efficient and versatile boats within the 16.5m registered length criterion than would have been possible under the old 25 ton rule.

Thus with an overall length of 59ft, registered length of 53.5ft, (just short of 16.5m), beam of 21.5ft, depth of 12.4ft and Part IV tonnage of 49.83 *Jasper II* was a much larger fuller vessel than she would have been at under 25 tons although she was not as huge as many of the under-60 footers which were to be built in subsequent years.

Last boat from Fraserburgh builder.

Built for Skipper George S. Forman of Peterhead, she was equipped for single and pair trawling for demersal and pelagic species and was powered by a Kelvin 280hp engine. Gear handling machinery included a Lossie Hydraulics trawl winch.

Furuno UK Ltd. supplied her fishfinders including FCV110 colour echosounder and FH106 sonar.

Jasper II was the last boat built by Noble before the yard closed down in the early 1980s. It had opened in 1932 to build ring netters and seiner drifters.

Chapter 5
INTO THE 1980s; BOATS ARE MORE FULL-BODIED AND CAPACIOUS

A new structure for the fishing industry

Another recession in the late 1970s brought about a shortfall in new boat building during the first few years of the '80s. Demand for fish caught by British boats fell for several reasons including an increase in imports resulting from the rising strength of sterling.

Things soon recovered.

But things soon recovered. In 1983 the member states of the European Community agreed on a revised Common Fisheries Policy. Britain fared quite well, being allowed to catch thirty-seven per cent of the total amount of fish to be taken annually by member states within EC waters.

At home, the Herring Industry Board and the White Fish Authority were replaced by the Sea Fish Industry Authority, with powers to modernise and develop the fishing industry. It played an important role in marketing and promoting fish, which helped increase consumer awareness of the product as a nutritious and enjoyable food.

Pressure stock licences.

There were new regulations however.

Member states of the EC were responsible for managing and enforcing national quotas and Britain required that boats over 10 metres registered length carried 'pressure stock licences', or PSLs, in order to be permitted to fish for species under quota.

Licences were granted mainly against the fishing history of the boats in order to restrict the growth in the number of vessels catching quota species. The ruling had little effect on orders for new boats as licences could be transferred from old vessels which had been withdrawn from fishing.

Quayside prices reached unprecedented figures, and the fleet's profit margin improved because of a slow-down in the rate of inflation and a drop in the cost of fuel.

The betterment in quayside prices together with grants from the Government and the EC gave a tremendous impetus to new boat building. Because of the strength of the white fish market the majority of new vessels were fitted out primarily for demersal fishing. More than a hundred white fish boats in the 39.9ft to 79.9ft registered length category were built for Scotland during the years 1983 to 1988 inclusively.

Fared less well.

For much of the 1980s the pelagic fleet fared less well than the white fish boats despite greater catching opportunities afforded by the re-opening of the North Sea herring grounds.

Owing to shortage of supplies in the 1970s many processors were not geared up to handle herring when the boats started catching again.

Many fishermen made mackerel their priority or else switched to white fish operations. More herring and mackerel were sold to Eastern Europe than to the home market.

The number of Scottish vessels normally engaged in pelagic fishing fell from around ninety in 1979 to only fifty or so in 1988, the majority being larger purser-trawlers upwards of 100ft long and big enough to cope with the disposition and whereabouts of the herring and mackerel shoals.

Huge purse seine fleet.

Throughout the 1970s there had been a continuing trend towards much bigger vessels in the purse seine fleet. As the majority were over 90ft registered length they are outside the scope of this book but a brief mention is made here.

By the close of 1978 Scotland owned some thirty-six

pursers with colossal fishing ability. All but three were built of steel and larger pursers measured 140ft long with engines of 1,600hp. About a dozen smaller and older ones had been lengthened to increase carrying capacity and fitted with CSW or RSW tanks to maintain the quality of their catches for longer periods.

Although herring landings were at an all-time low in 1978 owing to the North Sea herring ban, and seasonal closures and catch restrictions elsewhere as conservation measures, pursers played a big part in the mackerel fishery.

Taking place in the late summer off the Scottish west coast and in autumn and winter off the English West Country this had become the UK's biggest fishery.

Much of the catch for human consumption was sold direct to Eastern European and other overseas factory or freezer ships known as 'klondykers', which were barred from catching fish themselves within the EC's two hundred mile territorial waters.

Scarcity.

Despite the growing fortunes of the white fish fleet, the fishermen faced problems. A scarcity of fish caused them to search further afield, open up new fishing areas, make extended trips of sometimes ten to fourteen days, and carry on fishing in rougher weather.

Boats as small as 60ft worked exposed grounds such as Rockall 200 miles out in the Atlantic and some thirty hours steam from the north-west coast of Scotland.

So, new white fish boats were built to cope with these conditions and requirements. They were designed to be efficient and substantial, and economical to run, with greater sea range and fuel and catch carrying capabilities.

In their general design there was a refinement and development of ideas first explored in the 1970s.

Capacious.

Builders and naval architects developed capacious deep and beamy full-bodied vessels with an enormous amount of space on deck and below.

The three-quarter-length or full length enclosed shelterdeck was designed as an integral part of the boat with provision for shooting and hauling ropes and wires over the shelter top. Deck layout was arranged to keep gear and catch handling areas separate in the interests of safety, and deck machinery became easier and safer to use, and modified to handle heavier fishing gear.

New ideas in working warps and nets, and in taking aboard the cod end, were tried out and many boats had more than one set of gear ready for shooting as necessary which enabled them to quickly exploit the grounds and disposition of fish to the best advantage. Catch handling areas could be arranged and equipped to reduce hard manual work and improve catch quality.

Cooling plants or effective insulation became standard in the fishroom.

There were new configurations of deckhouse structures and gear handling machinery but, in the over 40ft length range, there was a very definite move away from the forward-wheelhouse design because it was more comfortable in rough weather to have wheelhouse and accommodation aft.

New fuel-saving engines were introduced and one or two boats of less than 60ft overall length had controllable pitch propellers.

Huge leaps forward in microprocessor science provided skippers with a vast range of sophisticated electronic instruments.

Crew accommodation was given prime consideration with even sixty-footers having several cabins. Fishermen asked for high standards of craftsmanship and finish, and the quality of work in the internal spaces of many boats reached luxury yacht standards.

There were useful advances in anti-corrosion technology and a range of treatments and coatings was developed for steel vessels.

Doubling the volume.

In the smaller size range the changes in skippers' ticket regulations from under-25 tons to below 16.5m registered length had a colossal effect on these boats, virtually doubling their volume with beneficial influence on stability, sea range, efficiency, endurance and general working arrangements.

Size for size.

There were a few more wooden-hulled boats than steel ones. Size for size, boats built of either material could now cost roughly the same, although few wooden ones were over 75ft long. The vast majority had transom sterns although there was a handful of wooden and steel vessels with cruiser sterns which looked very plump owing to the full and beamy hull lines.

Everyone concerned with fishing boat technology continued to look at further possibilities in every aspect of design and equipment. The Sea Fish Industry Authority published new 'Rules for the Construction of Wooden Fishing Vessels of Less than 24.4m Registered Length' and brought out rules for building boats in steel and GRP for the same registered length group.

The SFIA's Industrial Development Unit continued to look into ways of further increasing vessel efficiency, catch quality and crew safety, and the DTI made amendments to its 1975 safety rules.

New ideas in existing boats.

New ideas are often first tried out in existing boats and proved to be workable before being incorporated into new buildings. Usually it is the fishermen themselves who see the need for improvements and modify their vessels accordingly.

Skipper Robert Reid of *Fruitful Harvest III* PD247 looked for ways of eliminating hazards which had caused accidents on seine net vessels.

Although Skipper Reid was not the first to fit a gutting shelter he was among the first to both shoot and haul ropes over the top of this structure out of the way of crewmen gutting the catch on deck.

Later *Fruitful Harvest III* was fitted with an enclosed non weathertight shelterdeck which incorporated several improvements over those already fitted to other vessels.

Rather than ending just abaft the wheelhouse it was extended further aft and a bag hatch set into the starboard side below the A-frame seine net derrick on the casing.

Gilson winch.

This eliminated the earlier seiner practice of emptying the cod end onto the open deck at the quarters and dragging the catch through the after end of the shelter. A gilson winch was fitted on the casing top and controlled from the wheelhouse to work the gilson wire from the A-frame.

The arrangement enabled the cod end to be lifted aboard without anyone needing to be nearby where ropes might break or cleats fly loose and cause an injury. And the design of the hatch prevented the cod end from swinging about and knocking someone overboard when it was being untied to empty the fish out. Inside the bag hatch a hopper with sloping base caused the fish to slide forwards towards the gutting area.

Lifting seine rope stern rollers around was another risky job and so *Fruitful Harvest III* was fitted with fixed rollers mounted on a gantry just forward of the transom.

Fixed rollers.

Skipper Reid worked with the Sea Fish Industry Authority in evaluating two types of roller assembly designed to reduce wear on rollers and ropes. One consisted of two counterbalanced hanging blocks with a pivoting action which followed the run of the ropes.

The other assembly incorporated three vertical and two horizontal rollers, the large diameter of which showed a reduction in rope wear during a twelve month period. The presence of the centre roller kept the two ropes separate which also increased their life. Portable rollers had from necessity been light and small to enable them to be handled manually but this had caused an acute bend in the ropes when they were coming in at an angle to the boat, which decreased rope life by distorting the fibres.

Concepts developed further.

Several of these concepts have been developed further on new and existing vessels. Fixed towing gantries of various types came into use and almost all seiner trawlers now shoot and haul ropes and wires over the shelter top.

Tremendous advance.

Fruitful Harvest III was also one of two seiners chosen by Racal Decca to evaluate the new CVP3500 Colour Video Plotter which came into wide use in the 1980s.

Using microprocessor technology it was a tremendous advance on the 350T Track Plotter and dispensed with the paper charts on which a boat's movements were recorded.

Instead, pictorial navigational information was displayed in a choice of seven colours on a computer screen and stored on disc for future reference.

It provided the skipper with a simple and powerful means of recording successful fishing tows and seabed data, and so enabled the precise tow to be repeated around wrecks and rough ground. The boat's position, her current track, the track to follow, and topographical outlines could be shown on the screen.

A fibre optic light pen was used to select the required display from a 'menu' and to insert marks and waypoints representing the position of wrecks, dahns, rough ground and the like, directly onto the screen.

Up to 3500 waypoints and boat's tracks and topographical details could be stored on each side of a disc and a personal code number ensured against unauthorised use of the information. The picture, which was shown on a latitude/longitude grid, could be shown in a variety of scales.

When used with the Decca MNS2000 Navigator the plotter could indicate wrecks and waypoints in Decca co-ordinates.

Stout and roomy wooden hulled vessels

Great big boat for her length.

Throughout the 1980s Macduff Boatbuilding and Engineering Co. was the most productive builder of wooden hulled boats. It developed its own designs in response to the changing needs of the fishermen and one of the largest boats, the 75ft transom sterned seiner trawler *Fruitful Bough* PD109, was handed over to Skipper James West of Peterhead in 1986.

She represented the stage reached in the evolution of wooden hulled seiner trawler design at that time, with many of the sensible ideas first explored in the 1970s being refined and rationalised to produce a really practical vessel.

Built to a new lines plan *Fruitful Bough* was a great big boat for her length with beamy, deep and full hull form and tonnage under Scottish Part IV Registry of 61.85.

Skipper West wanted an adaptable boat equally capable of single boat and pair trawling or seine netting.

When I visited her in 1987 she had worked as a seiner and pair trawler making trips of less than a week from Peterhead and catching mainly cod, haddock, whiting and coley.

She had fished all over the North Sea and her biggest catches had been 480 to 490 boxes.

Skipper West said she was a good seaboat. He told me 'I wouldn't change her. One night in 1986 we were in a force 10 gale. We kept her head to the weather for four hours and the shelterdeck kept the water away. She took very little on the top deck.'

Measuring 74.35ft x 22.96ft x 13ft she was of stouter construction and had a larger propeller aperture than earlier vessels of similar length, and the deck was planked with iroko which was stronger than Oregon pine formerly used for decking.

Bag hatch.

Her three-quarter-length aluminium non-weathertight shelterdeck was designed from the outset as an integral part of the superstructure.

It extended to the after end of the steel casing which was offset to port with the aluminium wheelhouse mounted atop on the centreline. The bag hatch was set

***Fruitful Bough** PD109 was a typical 75ft wooden hulled seiner trawler built in the mid 1980s.
Skipper West said she was an excellent seaboat.*

into the starboard side of the shelterdeck forward of the wheelhouse and adjacent to the fish handling area.

This was by now a location favoured by many shelterdeckers for lifting aboard the cod ends of trawls, but *Fruitful Bough* also emptied her seine net bag here rather than in the traditional flydragging seiner position at the quarters so that fish was not dragged around so much on deck. This improved catch quality and gave the crew less work.

A hydraulic ram raised and lowered the hinged hatch cover and the cod end was hoisted up by use of a stout derrick and gilson winch on the shelter top and emptied into a reception bin from which fish was taken out through sliding shutters.

After gutting, the fish was placed in a washer made by the builders to a Sea Fish Industry Authority design. Two water inlets produced a swirling action which improved cleaning efficiency.

In the fish handling area, where loss of footing could be dangerous, strips of Granogrip were applied to the deck. Made by Belzona Molecular Ltd. this safety grip system had first been used for fishing vessel application on the Lossiemouth seiner *Emma Thomson II* INS277 some three years previously, since when four hundred new and existing boats had been treated.

Fishroom cooling.

Insulated with cork on the after bulkhead and polystyrene on the deckhead, and lined with timber and fitted with aluminiun stanchions and pound boards, the fishroom could carry 975 boxes of fish.

It was equipped with a Seacool cooling system using eutectic plate evaporators. Eutectic plates retain cooling properties for a period after the plant has been shut down.

More fishermen were realising the benefits of cooling systems, finding generally a twenty-five to thirty per cent reduction in their ice requirements and a definite improvement in catch condition and market prices.

As now customary with cooling plants, *Fruitful Bough*'s evaporators cooled all the fishroom rather than just the after section. By early 1987 Seacool Ltd. had fitted some 150 systems to new and existing vessels.

New Kelvin engine.

Fruitful Bough was powered by the new Kelvin eight cylinder turbo charged and after cooled TGSC8 engine of 650hp at 1350 rpm turning a 69in Bruntons fixed pitch propeller throgh a Reintjes WAV500 gearbox of 4:1 reduction ratio and Fleetwoods 5.75in diameter sterngear.

Kelvin had introduced the TGSC8 two years previously to meet the requirements of skippers who were looking for fuel-saving reliable compact engines with sufficient horsepower to enable them to work further afield for longer periods and bring back bigger catches. The engine had a re-designed cylinder head and block to maximise fuel economy and was said by the makers to show a ten per cent reduction in fuel consumption over earlier models.

An Enviro Systems Fuel Stretcher with wheelhouse monitor indicated the amount of fuel being used so that the engine could be run at its most economical speed.

The sterngear was the first of a new size from Henry Fleetwood and Sons of Lossiemouth, which had been making propeller shafts for more than fifty years.

A Transmotor 110V generator, two Transmotor 24V alternators, and an emergency net retrieve pump, and rope reel brake pump and the steering gear pump were powered from the engine.

Another Transmotor 110V generator, Transmotor 24V alternator, Gilbert Gilkes and Gordon GGG 250/700 bilge and general service pump and the Abex Denison hydraulic pumps for the deck machinery were powered by the Volvo Penta TD100 CHC auxiliary engine rated at 215hp and 1500 rpm.

By this time Volvo was enjoying a large slice of auxiliary engine sales to meet the demand for more powerful units able to drive primary hydraulic pumps in addition to generators and bilge pumps. Another GGG bilge and general service pump, and a Desmi fuel transfer pump were electrically driven.

Three tanks carried in total 3,000 gallons of fuel oil.

Load sense.

Fruitful Bough's deck machinery was supplied by Thistle Marine Ltd. of Peterhead and included two-drum trawl winch, seine winch, split net drum and a gilson winch from Oilpower A/S of Denmark, and two seine rope reels, 24in W-sheave power block and a landing winch of the Scottish firm's own manufacture.

Split net drums are divided into two sections each with its own motor. The net can be stored evenly because adjustments can be made to the two sections of net drum when the bridles are being hauled.

Stronger hydraulic system.

Designed to hold 750 fathoms of 18mm wire the trawl winch was positioned athwartships well forward below the shelterdeck with the guide-on gear angled upwards to work the wires over the shelter top. The two-barrel seine winch was mounted on a pedestal abaft the trawl winch, followed by the two rope reels each able to carry 28 coils of 3½in rope, although *Fruitful Bough* normally used thirteen coils of 3¾in rope each side.

A trawl net was carried on the net drum offset to port on the afterdeck and the power block was hung from an Atlas short post crane mounted on the after end of the shelterdeck.

All this deck machinery was stronger than similar fittings of ten years earlier, requiring more powerful, faster running pumps with a higher working pressure.

Thistle designed the hydraulic system. An Abex Denison P14 variable delivery pump powered the seine and trawl winches and net drum through an open loop hydraulic circuit. The pump had 'load sense' so that it adjusted its oil flow to the requirements of the trawl winch and net drum during trawling operations, thereby eliminating the need for complicated change-over controls, and improving the efficiency of both units.

Open loop circuits had the advantage that new deck units could be added without too much difficulty.

An Abex Denison fixed displacement double pump drove the other hydraulic equipment through a secondary circuit.

Hydraulic towing gantries.

Seine ropes and trawl wires were shot and hauled over the shelterdeck through cowls.

In place of portable seine rope towing rollers, *Fruitful Bough* used one or other of two gantries on the after end of the shelterdeck, featuring cage-type rollers which were moved along parallel bars into the required position by means of hydraulic rams.

A number of seiners were trying out various types of hydraulic gantries and rollers around this time.

Fruitful Bough's ropes were payed out through small hanging blocks atop the post-type trawl gallows which were fitted abaft the shelterdeck.

The wheelhouse, which slightly overlapped the fore end of the casing, was flared at sides and front.

Reflecting the huge leaps forward in microprocessor technology in the 1980s, *Fruitful Bough* carried some seventeen electronic instruments.

Fishfinders comprised Elac LAZ 2310 Colour Image Scope and Sumar V-11 Colour Sounder. The latter operated on the frequencies of 50 and 200 kHz and showed echoes in eight colours on an 11in rectangular screen. Low frequency soundings are suitable for deep water fishing whereas high frequency is best for finding small fish in shallow water.

Features offered by the Colour Image Scope included a 'hard bottom analiser' with an alarm which indicated that the net might be in danger of snagging. A 'biomass display' showed fish density on a bar graph which, like a thermometer, went up with increasing fish density.

Communications were handled by a Sailor T2031 R2022 Compact Series SSB radiotelephone, RT144C VHF radiotelephone and R501 watch receiver, Woodsons talk back system, and an ICOM 1C-M80 radiotelephone.

The Compact Series SSB radiotelephone was part of a new small, yet powerful, system from S. P. Sailor, using touch pad controls and digital frequency readouts.

Navigation instruments included Decca Mk 21 Navigator, 350T Track Plotter, NP 21 latitude/longitude converter, Vigil RM radar, Shipmate RS4000 Navigator, Plotter Adaptor, Koden colour radar and Robertson AP40 Autopilot.

The Shipmate RS4000 was a radio navigator which showed the boat's position in degrees latitude and longitude and Decca lanes, and was used with the Plotter Adaptor to superimpose navigational information such as the boat's track when steaming and fishing, and the location of waypoints such as dahns, onto the Koden radar picture.

A Marinefax weather chart recorder from Alden Electronics provided a print-out of the complete weather situation and forecast in the interests of safety and better fish catching efficiency.

Weather charts of every description were broadcast regularly from shore based transmitter sites and, for example, would give ocean current and sea temperature information which could affect the whereabouts of fish, whereas prognosis charts showed existing and forecast positions of weather highs and lows and their speed and direction of movement, and gave storm warnings.

Access.

Other fittings included Tenfjord H115 steering gear, two Bostrom Viking chairs, C. C. Jensen windows with Wynstruments wiper, Lilley and Gillie compass, Kobelt engine controls, Ben log, and monitors for the closed circuit TV cameras near the winches and in the engineroom.

Access into the wheelhouse was gained from the shelterdeck or from within the casing below. Facilities in the casing included Kempsafe electric cooker and a shower, washbasin and a lavatory. Six hundred gallons of fresh water were carried in the bow.

Four cabins.

Below deck, layout was conventional except for the aft accommodation which was imaginatively laid out with two three-berth, one two-berth and a single berth cabin. Electric heaters were fitted in cabin and wheelhouse. A Francis 12in searchlight and Chalmit decklights were carried.

In keeping with safety requirements *Fruitful Bough* carried two ten-man RDF liferafts, Halon 1301 fire smothering system, Marinex fire and bilge level detection and alarm system, and Electronics Devices refrigerant gas detector.

Much roomier boats below 16.5 metres

Some very capacious boats were designed and built under the new below-16.5 registered length ruling.

Replacing the under-25 Registered Tons Part IV criterion the new legislation gave much greater scope to this important sector of the fleet.

The old regulations had put severe restrictions on the volume of enclosed space in these boats but now the registered length was the only limiting factor.

Builders could now produce much roomier vessels with more beam and depth in proportion to their length, giving them greater carrying capacities and fishing capabilities together with better living and working conditions for the fishermen.

And the additional stability afforded by the beamier, deeper, fuller hulls enabled them to have shelterdecks and provided new possibilities in the layout and positioning of superstructure and gear handling machinery.

Helenus.

Macduff Boatbuilding produced eight wooden hulled transom sterned trawlers and seiner trawlers below 16.5m registered length. All were built to the same hull lines.

The pair trawler *Helenus* BCK64 delivered in 1987 to Skipper Albert Farquhar of Portknockie was the seventh in the series.

Main measurements of *Helenus*, when compared with those of an average below-25 ton boat, designed under the old Ticket rules, show the advances made possible by the new regulations.

Under-25 Tons Part IV		*Helenus*
Length Overall	56ft (17.08m).	61.66ft (18.80m).
Registered Length	51ft (15.55m).	53.23ft (16.23m).
Beam	18.50ft (5.64m).	22ft (6.71m).
Moulded Depth	9ft (2.75m).	13ft (4m).
Light Ship		
Displacement Tonnage	65 to 75.	145.
Registered Tons Part IV	24.5.	48.26.
Horsepower	230 to 350.	400.

Designed to come below 16.5m registered length **Helenus** *BCK64 had almost twice the volume when compared with boats of similar length which were built under the old 25 tons criterion. Note her depth in proportion to her length.*

Helenus was built of larch on oak with iroko deck and steel beams. Her weathertight steel casing was set athwartships from rail to rail with weathertight doors in her forward and after bulkheads.

Weathertight.

Extending forward from the casing the aluminium shelterdeck was non weathertight with the hydraulically operated bag hatch set into the starboard side. The forecastle section at the stem was weathertight being separated from the fish handling area by a bulkhead containing a weathertight door.

The aluminium wheelhouse was set on the centreline above casing and shelter.

In the interests of safety the deck machinery and gear handling operations were separate from the catch handling area. Two neat and low set Rapp split trawl winches were positioned port and starboard at shelter deck level to either side of the specially contoured wheelhouse

The winches were angled outwards to give the warps a straight run to the gallows blocks which were hung from stout cantilever arms affixed at either end of a transverse frame on the after end of the shelter.

Controls for winch, main and auxiliary engines and steering gear were set on a console in the after end of the wheelhouse from where the skipper could see the after deck area.

A Rapp 24in wide-sheave power block was hung from an Atlas short-post crane abaft the wheelhouse and a Rapp split net drum lay on the main deck aft.

A central towing point for the warps was fitted on the after casing bulkhead, a two-barrel whipping winch for use with this being mounted nearby.

Cod ends were taken forward with the help of a similar winch on the forecastle bulkhead below the shelter. They were hoisted through the bag hatch by use of a stout pole-type fish derrick and gilson winch.

Used solely for fish handling the foredeck was laid out across its full width with steel stanchions and aluminium pound boards and equipped with a fixed fish washer. A stainless steel chute led to the fishroom hatch. Two Faaborg pumps, one automatic and the other worked manually, cleared water from the catch handling area. Below deck, layout was traditional, with steel bulkheads, but the aft accommodation was divided into four separate cabins.

The fishroom had a Seacool, cooling system.

Triple pump.

Helenus was powered by a Caterpillar engine of 400hp at 1600rpm, turning a 64in diameter Bruntons propeller through a 5:1 reduction gearbox.

A fixed delivery Voith triple hydraulic pump was powered through a clutch from the Caterpillar 210hp auxiliary engine. The two larger sections of pump drove the split winches and net drum and the smaller section the rest of the deck machinery.

Fixed delivery double pumps were preferable to variable delivery types for driving split winches. Each section of pump fed one split winch and both sections of pump delivered oil at the same rate enabling the winch motors to run at identical speeds and haul in the trawl evenly.

Electrics were 110V DC, and some 2,400 gallons of fuel oil were carried.

Electronic instruments included a C Tech FFC-2000 colour fishfinder, Simrad SL Sonar and CM Sonarscope, and a Racal Decca CVP3500 colour video plotter with MNS2000 Navigator.

The sides of the shelter abaft the casing were set inboard to leave a space to accommodate trawl doors should *Helenus* work single boat trawls.

Helenus pair trawled for white fish on west coast grounds in partnership with *Atlas* BF245 handed over by the same builder earlier in 1987 to Skipper Bill West, who was Skipper Farquhar's son-in-law. *Atlas* was identical to *Helenus* in almost all particulars differing mainly in some items of wheelhouse equipment.

The unusual layout of *Helenus* and *Atlas* was first used in the third boat in the series. She was *Seagull* BF83, built in 1983 for Skipper Kenneth West.

Hefty sixty-footer from 'Herdies'.

These new stout below-16.5m boats were certainly liked by the fishermen.

In 1986 Herd and Mackenzie delivered the 60ft wooden-hulled trawler *Unity II* BCK35 to Skipper John Flett of Buckie. His son William, who sailed as mate, put many of his own ideas into her planning. Both men were delighted with her and said she was a first class seaboat.

Safety and efficiency were given priority and manual work for the crewmen was reduced where possible. In order to keep the trawl warps clear of the crew members the Rapp split trawl winches were housed port and starboard in enclosed compartments beneath the after end of the shelterdeck with the warps leading upwards via a trunking through the shelter top and around sheaves to the trawl blocks.

A Rapp split net drum was on the afterdeck and same-make 24in W-sheave power block was affixed to a short-post Atlas crane on the after end of the shelterdeck.

Set on the centreline atop the three-quarter-length non weathertight shelterdeck the aluminium wheelhouse gave virtually all round visibility with a good view of net hauling and shooting.

The steel casing spanned the boat's width with a passage leading through from afterdeck to fish handling area.

Bag hatch.

The bag hatch with sliding shutter was set into the starboard side of the shelter forward of amidships beneath a tripod gilson derrick worked by a gilson winch. Cod ends were emptied into an aluminium reception hopper from which fish were taken out and gutted on a

Unity II BCK35 was another stout below-16.5m boat.
Her split trawl winches were located below the after end of her shelterdeck
in the interests of safety.

tray, and then placed in the washer from where they passed by gravity down a chute to a table in the fishroom for grading and boxing.

Able to carry some 450 boxes her fishroom was insulated on sides, deckhead and bulkheads and under the hatchcover by Hirtshals Skumisolering of Denmark. Using polyurethane foam covered in GRP it was designed to keep the catch in good condition without a cooling plant and maintain the ice at a steady temperature. Coming below the 16.5m registered length measurement *Unity II* had a beam of 22ft 2in, moulded depth of 11ft 8in and Part IV tonnage of 44.65.

Her Caterpillar 495hp engine had a 6:1 reduction gear and 69in fixed pitch propeller.

Power for the Voith and Vickers hydraulic pumps for the deck machinery was transmitted through a Norgear front end gearbox. *Unity II* carried an impressive amount of electronic equipment and many of the instruments were set into neat, easy to clean consoles designed to her owner's requirements.

Fishfinders comprised JRC JFV-216 dual frequency colour echosounder and JRC JFZ-200 paper echosounder from Japan Radio Co. Ltd. and supplied by Sait Marine Ltd. The JFV-216 presented images in gradations of either eight or sixteen colours and had a large capacity memory which enabled three past recordings and the current picture to be displayed simultaneously. It offered a choice of sounding frequencies, but *Unity II*'s set operated on 28 and 200 kHz and the paper sounder used its own 50kHz transducer.

She also carried a JRC-JAX2 weather forecast chart receiver which Skipper Flett said was 'a useful thing'.

Communications equipment included Skanti TRP8250 SSB radiotelephone which was designed to satisfy the

*The stalwart and capacious little trawler **Sea Spray II** PD245 is also under 16.5m. Note the A-frame gilson derrick above her bag hatch.*

__Faithful__ FR129 on the slipway in Fraserburgh after a repaint. Her beam extends for much of her length. Note her full lines and deep bilges. Because her shelterdeck is classed as weathertight her bag hatches are in the shelter top rather than in the side.

expected future international requirements for HF (long range) radiotelephony.

Unity II made trips of some four to seven days duration, up to sixty miles from Kinlochbervie which, lying south of Cape Wrath is Britain's most remote mainland port.

Many east coast skippers chose to work from this desolate tiny village owing to its nearness to lucrative fishing grounds. Around fifty boats were based there in the early 1980s and major improvements to harbour and fish market were carried out as the decade progressed.

Full bodied.

These below-16.5m registered length boats were as beamy as the 75 footers built fifteen years previously. The very deep and full bodied wooden hulled *Sea Spray II* PD245 designed by naval architects S. C. McAllister and Co. and built by Gerrard Brothers in 1986 for Peterhead skipper William McIntosh measured 59.98ft overall with 22.36ft beam and 47.12 Part IV tonnage.

Despite her stoutness she averaged 11¼ knots on her trials. Her compact MAN- B&W Alpha 495hp and 1800rpm engine turned a controllable pitch propeller.

Built to work slightly longer trips further afield than her 54ft predecessor, *Sea Spray II* had three-quarter-length non weathertight shelterdeck, with hydraulic bag hatch in the starboard side beneath a tall A-frame derrick with gilson winch. Her deck was roomy with steel casing offset to port and Jensen winch forward. Warps were worked over the shelter top.

Capacious.

Larger wooden hulled boats were also immensely capacious. My photograph of the seiner trawler *Faithful* FR129 on Fraserburgh slipway shows her full form.

Delivered in 1985 to skipper Stewart Buchan she measured 77ft overall with 23ft beam and 14ft extreme depth and was one of a series of transom sterned boats built by J. and G. Forbes to a new hull model designed by the Napier Co.

Her lines were fuller and beamier and deeper than boats of similar length built by Forbes at the start of the decade, with her beam carried along for more of her length.

Faithful was arranged mainly for seining with winch and rope reels forward. Her bag hatches were set port and starboard in the top of her weathertight shelterdeck at the quarters with A-frame derricks and gilson winch atop the casing.

Chapter 6
VARIATIONS IN DESIGN, AND THE FULL-LENGTH SHELTERDECK

No such thing.

There is no such thing as a standard seiner trawler and each skipper had his own opinions on suitable deck layout and general working arrangements.

The 75ft *Solan* BCK195 built by Macduff Boatbuilding in 1984 had her wheelhouse on the after end of her casing. It gave Skipper Leslie Findlay the best overall view of gear handling operations on the afterdeck, and the cod end being discharged into one or other of the two bag hatches which were set into the non weathertight shelterdeck forward of the wheelhouse.

The aft wheelhouse idea was first seen in *Adelphi* built in 1976, but the shelterdeck gave *Solan* a much more pleasing appearance.

Built to a new design from Macduff the transom sterned *Solan* was particularly hefty with broad beam of 23.50ft and catch carrying capacity for a thousand boxes.

Her three rope reels each carried fifteen coils of 3½in rope.

Safer and easier.

Other ideas on making gear and catch handling safer and easier were explored in the 75ft transom sterned *Crystal River* BCK16 delivered from Jones Buckie Shipyard to Skipper Peter Smith in 1985.

Her Rapp split trawl winches were set well aft just within the after end of her shelterdeck. As a compromise between the traditional aft position for seining and forward for trawling her bag hatch was set just forward of amidships on the starboard side of her non weathertight shelter.

Cod ends were thus emptied adjacent to the gutting area thereby giving the crew less work and preventing fish damage. The wooden hulled *Crystal River* was built to a new deeper, fuller and beamier hull design from S. C. McAllister, measuring 74.21ft overall with beam of 23ft and draft of 12ft.

Seine winch and rope reels were forward and ropes worked over the shelter top. Partitions abaft the reels prevented mud from the ropes polluting the catch. Her casing was offset to port with roomy wheelhouse set on the after end on the centreline. A closed circuit TV system had cameras focussed on the trawl winches and seine winch and reels.

A 500 gallon fresh water tank was forward thereby helping to maintain correct trim as the fishroom filled up and fresh water was consumed.

Simplicity.

Herd and Mackenzie handed over the 65ft transom sterned wooden hulled seiner *Hope* BCK59 to Skipper Gordon McKay of Buckie on Christmas Eve 1986.

Skipper McKay liked to make trips of only three or four days and normally sailed on Sunday night and landed at Peterhead on Thursday morning.

He had planned *Hope* with simplicity, safety and economy in mind and was very pleased with her handling qualities and low fuel consumption. She showed herself to be very manoeuvrable with a tight turn which was useful when coming up to the dahn and when moving around in Peterhead's hectically busy harbour.

Peterhead was by now the leading white fish port in Europe. Demersal landings from British vessels were valued at just over £63 million in 1988 compared with less than £1 million in 1969. The fish market which is open six days a week can handle more than 10,000 boxes daily.

During 1988 white fish was put ashore from more than six hundred boats including around three hundred from Moray Firth ports.

This rapid and phenomenal rise began late in 1970 when seine net skippers began a boycott of Aberdeen in protest against high landing charges.

Hope's layout and beaminess provided a lot of room

Hope BCK59 *was arranged so that her crew need seldom go on the shelter top. The openings in the shelter were designed so that ropes could be transferred from shooting rollers to hauling sheaves from beneath the shelter.*

for a 65-footer both on deck and below. Although she was 5ft shorter than his previous command, the 70ft x 20ft cruiser sterned *Rosemount* BCK277 built in 1962, Skipper McKay said that *Hope* had a lot more deck space and double the carrying capacity with room for seven hundred boxes in her fishroom.

Under cover.

Hope measured just over 65ft long with beam of 21ft 6in and moulded depth of 11ft 10in. Her casing was offset to port with the wheelhouse on the centreline atop the non-weathertight shelterdeck, which extended well aft to afford some shelter on the after deck without obstructing the skipper's view of net handling.

Seine net ropes were set and hauled over the shelterdeck out of the way of the crewmen who worked under cover except when setting and retrieving the dahn, setting

and hauling aboard the net, and drying up the net with the power block.

In the interests of safety the crewmen seldom went on the shelterdeck top. Instead of having separate hatches in the shelter top for shooting and hauling the ropes, *Hope* had two hatches each containing a shooting roller and hauling sheave. This arrangement enabled a man to transfer rope from roller to sheave from below the shelter.

Mounted port and starboard on the after end of the shelter were two pendulum shooting and hauling gantries similar to the one in use on *Fruitful Harvest III*. The two counter-balanced hanging blocks swivelled in accordance with the run of the ropes and the pendulum action brought the blocks together as the ropes converged during hauling.

They were easier to maintain than the hydraulically operated rollers used by some vessels.

112

New Gardner engine.

Hope was the first new Scottish vessel supplied with the Gardner 6LYT1 turbo charged six-cylinder diesel engine on which the makers had begun development in 1978. It produced 310hp at 1600rpm and drove the FAL Scottish Propeller Service 68in propeller through a Twin Disc 6:1 reduction gearbox and 4½in sterngear.

Important design features included compact size, quiet running, and fuel efficiency, and Skipper McKay said *Hope* only used 700 gallons a week as against 1,000 consumed by some boats.

The engine was supplied by Henry Fleetwood and Sons of Lossiemouth who started business some fifty-three years earlier as Gardner's Scottish agents. Gardner had first installed propulsion engines in Scottish fishing boats in the early 1900s, and in the late 1950s enjoyed some seventy-five per cent of the market for vessels within the Gardner horsepower range of 28 to 152hp.

Supplied by Fishing Hydraulics *Hope's* seine winch and two rope reels were positioned on the main deck forward and power block and crane atop the shelter aft. The bag hatch was set into the starboard side of the shelter forward of the wheelhouse.

Fleetwood also supplied the Gardner 6LXB auxiliary engine of 127hp at 1500 rpm which drove a 24V alternator and GGG pump and the Voith double hydraulic pump for the seine and gilson winches and the Vickers pump for rope reels, power block and landing winch. As the Voith pump was of fixed delivery type the seine winch was given variable speed through a pressure compensated valve. The pump was fitted to enable *Hope* to switch to trawling if required, with split winches maybe fitted on the shelter's after end.

Electrics were 24V for simplicity.

Insulation.

Fitted with aluminium stanchions and pound boards the fishroom was insulated hy Hirtshals Skumisolering.

The wheelhouse provided virtually all-round visibility, and layout was planned to avoid having a conglomeration of things scattered everywhere. Primary fishfinding, navigation and communications equipment was arranged in consoles within easy reach of the skipper's chair, with smaller instruments set into a panel above the windows.

The Sumar V-11 colour video sounder operated on two frequencies of 50 and 200kHz. A Racal Decca CVP-3500 colour video plotter was used with the new Decca Mk53 Navigator which gave readouts in latitude and longitude as well as Decca co-ordinates.

Bonaventure.

Other boats were equipped primarily for trawling.

In 1987 Herd and Mackenzie built the wooden hulled sister ships *Bonaventure* LH111 and *Rebecca* LH11 for Skippers Tom Bain and Robert Millar. Each skipper had a half share in the other's boat. Although virtually identical in most respects the boats varied in wheelhouse layout and choice of electronics.

They were designed for working demersal pair trawls together since seining had become less productive on the central North Sea grounds worked by the Eyemouth fleet.

They both towed their gear from the starboard side as their skippers found this helped pair trawlers to maintain their position and keep the net open.

Bonaventure was the first to be completed. She was built to a new design from 'Herdies' with the beam carried for much of her length. She measured just short of 71ft overall with 22ft beam and moulded depth of 12ft, and the standard of workmanship and finish throughout the boat was superb. Her non weathertight aluminium shelterdeck extended well aft and had a steel section at the after end.

Skipper Bain's decision to tow gear from starboard and haul the cod end aboard at the port side influenced the layout and design of the superstructure and gear handling equipment.

In contrast to most boats the bag hatch and gilson derrick were sited to port forward and casing offset to starboard. The port bag hatch was also suitable for

Bonaventure LHIII leaving Buckie for sea trials in 1987.
Her bag hatch was offset to port forward of the wheelhouse rather than in the more usual position to starboard.
Note the position of the power block crane and net drum on the after end of the shelterdeck.

conditions in Eyemouth where vessels unload with their starboard sides adjacent to the quay. Thus the gilson derrick was clear of the landing derrick when the boxes of fish were being swung ashore.

A net drum from North Sea Winches of Scarborough was set atop the after end of the shelterdeck allowing the net to be flaked down onto the afterdeck for repair, and was offset slightly to starboard in line with a shooting and hauling roller fitted on the transom rail.

In order to give the Rapp W-sheave power block a good

reach round towards the bag hatch the Atlas short-post crane was located to port of the net drum.

Mounted athwartships well forward on the main deck the North Sea Winches four drum trawl winch carried the single heavy trawl warp on the starboard main drum, and on the port main drum a lighter messenger wire used for retrieving the sweeps from the partner vessel when the net was being hauled aboard.

Lifting wire.

A lifting wire for the cod end was carried on the port auxiliary drum. All the wires were worked through individual fairleads set into the shelter top, including the cod end lifting wire which passed through a block at the top of the gilson derrick.

The trawl warp was towed from a block hung from a stout wire slung athwartships between the gallows.

The block slid along the wire in accordance with the tide to make towing easier.

Electronics included Simrad sonar giving readings in eight colours. It was used primarily to determine the nature of the seabed as Skipper Bain preferred to work over rough ground.

Bonaventure's cabin was luxurious. Framed prints of Scottish castles hung on the bulkheads and the coal-effect electric fire had a wooden mantlepiece surround with a mirror above.

She was powered by a Caterpillar 495hp engine which also drove the hydraulic pumps for the deck gear.

Over the top.

There were various ways of working seine ropes and trawl warps. Although the seiner trawler *Moray Endurance* BCK34 was equipped to shoot and retrieve ropes and warps over the shelter top, she normally hauled the seine ropes along the main deck via stern rollers, casing-side rollers, and midships leads in the traditional manner. Skipper Tommy Ritchie said this caused less rope wear and gave a better lead.

At times of heavy fishing the ropes were hauled over the shelter to keep them clear of crewmen gutting fish on deck.

All the specialised rollers, blocks and fairleads for rope hauling and shooting were made by Flemings Fairleads of Buckie, formerly the rope and wire division of Lockwood Torday and Carlisle of North Shields, which had introduced the successful rail-mounted hauling roller in the late 1970s.

Flemings now supplied a wide range of blocks, rollers, sheaves and fairleads for trawlers and flydragging seiners.

Moray Endurance had stern rollers, shooting rollers, mid-shelter rollers, shooting blocks, wheelhouse rollers and fairlead assemblies all of corrosion resistant materials designed to withstand the abrasion from seine net ropes which get full of sand from the seabed.

She had no bag hatches. Cod ends were lifted aboard at port and starboard quarter by use of the A-frame derrick and one of two gilson winches on the casing top.

The last cruiser sterns.

Delivered in May 1986 from George Thomson and Son of Buckie *Moray Endurance* was one of only half a dozen wooden hulled boats built in the 1980s to have a cruiser stern.

Two others were *Conquest* BCK157 and *Shalimar* INS184 built by Thomson in 1984 and 1985 respectively.

In the 1930s Thomson had built some of the earliest large cruiser sterned motor herring drifters including the 77ft *Poppy* BCK41 in 1934. The drawing of *Poppy*, renamed *Cairntoul* in Chapter 1 shows her narrow-gutted lines which were in strong contrast to the plump and deep and beamy shelterdecked shapes of *Conquest, Shalimar* and *Moray Endurance*

Five feet beamier.

At 75ft x 23ft these three were almost 5ft beamier than *Poppy*, and their beam was continued for sixty per cent of their length, giving them much fuller lines. They had a Part IV Registered Tonnage of almost 70 and could hold

Moray Endurance BCK34 *was one of only a handful of wooden-hulled boats built in the 1980s to have a cruiser stern. Her shelterdeck did not extend so far aft as that on many boats built at that time and the cod end was emptied onto the open deck at the quarters.*

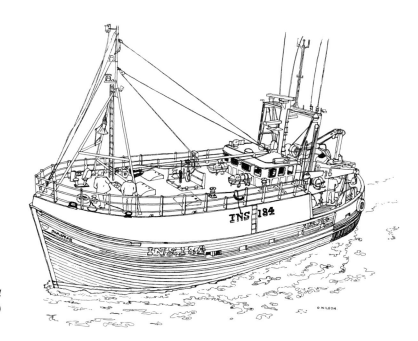

Compare the full and beamy shape of **Shalimar** *INS184 with the narrow gutted lines of* **Cairntoul** *(Chapter 1) built by the same builder fifty years earlier.*

1,000 boxes of fish. They were designed by S. C. McAllister in conjunction with their owners and builders and had non-weathertight shelters and 495hp Kelvin engines.

Conquest was fitted with a prototype seine rope towing assembly from Flemings Fairleads. Basically it comprised a towing roller moved hydraulically along a beam mounted on her trawl gallows. It enabled the angle of the ropes to be adjusted when being hauled over her shelter top.

All three had winch and rope reels forward and deckhouse on the centreline and were equipped with fishroom cooling plants.

Another wooden hulled cruiser sterner from this time was the 76ft *Tyleana* BF61. Skipper Iain Philip thought a cruiser stern produced a better seaboat.

Built in 1986 by Macduff Boatbuilding, *Tyleana* had similar lines and dimensions to *Fruitful Bough* except for her stern. Her deckhouse was set on the centreline and bag hatches set port and starboard in the after end of her non-weathertight shelter. Ropes and wires were worked over the shelter top.

Largest.

The largest wooden hulled boat from the 1980s was the 86ft transom sterned seiner trawler *Marconn II* FR376, built by J. and G. Forbes in 1987 for Skipper George Bruce of Fraserburgh. Her beam was just under 24ft so that she would not be too beamy to get on the Fraserburgh slipway for repair and overhaul rather than using far more costly dry-dock facilities.

Full length shelterdecks.

By the middle of the 1980s the three-quarter-length shelterdeck had become a standard feature on trawlers and seiner trawlers in the 50ft to 86ft size range, but the concept was taken further with the completion of the first with full length shelters in 1985.

One such was the 88ft Peterhead seiner trawler *Sundari*

PD93 built by Johs Kristensen Skibsbyggeri in Denmark for Skipper William Morgan and his son James, as a replacement to their 86ft vessel of the same name, built at the John Lewis yard in 1972.

Although only 2ft longer the new boat was 3ft beamier and much deeper than her predecessor and very different in appearance and layout. Her arrangement enabled nets to be worked from main deck or shelter-deck and two sets of gear could be fully rigged and ready for use as required, so saving a lot of time on rough ground when nets could get damaged.

In shabby weather the gear was handled from below the shelter. Owing to fish scarcity *Sundari* often worked harder ground some three hundred miles away from home, spending eight to ten days at sea as opposed to trips of a week or less made by her predecessor.

Workable ideas.

When planning *Sundari* father and son gave careful thought to safety, efficiency, versatility, automation and catch quality.

She proved their ideas to be sound and workable and James said that they were well pleased with her.

Her unusual features included a hydraulically driven fish conveyor and a new type of seine net winch.

As far as possible the fishing gear was separated from the fish handling area and the shelterdeck gave the fishermen maximum cover and could be enclosed when the boat was dodging in rough seas, or making a passage.

Sundari's main dimensions were 88ft x 24.10ft x 12.80ft moulded depth and she was of all welded steel construction with round bilges and transom stern. Her wheelhouse was just aft of amidships and a stout gantry spanned the deck just forward of the transom.

Except for the split trawl winches all the gear handling machinery was aft. Located centrally on the shelter abaft the wheelhouse the seine winch was a prototype from Norlau A/S of Denmark, designed to reduce wear on ropes and winch drive.

It had two grooved hauling barrels on each side so that

Sundari PD93 taking on ice in Peterhead. Note her full length shelterdeck, and the gilson derrick above her bag hatch abaft the wheelhouse. Also note the two white pipes through which the starboard trawl warp travels aft along the shelter top to the towing block.

each rope travelled around two barrels and was prevented by the grooves from overlapping. James said that the winch was working fine and certainly prolonged rope life.

Two seine rope reels from Grenaa Smedie og Maskinfabrik A/S of Denmark, each capable of holding twenty-six coils of 3¾in rope, were sited on the main deck abaft the casing.

Flemings portable cage type seine rope stern rollers were mounted on the bulwark aft and shooting blocks with nylon sheaves were hung under the stern gantry. Seine ropes came in through the stern rollers and via leads to the winch and thence over rollers and down onto the reels through slots in the shelterdeck.

Reels and casing were offset to port to leave room to starboard for the fish reception area. A Norlau split net

drum was positioned on the centreline abaft the reels and the same-make split trawl winches were fitted on the main deck well forward.

A small Norlau electrically powered winch, near the net drum, was used for handling the dog rope when pair trawling. A Norlau hydraulic landing winch and windlass were also carried.

The trawl winches' guiding-on gear was angled upwards to enable the wires to go up through slots and aft through steel tubes arranged along the shelterdeck to towing blocks on the stern gantry.

'It saves the back'.

A Rapp 24in power block with double sheave was hung from an Atlas crane mounted on the stern gantry.

There were three net bins right aft on the shelterdeck

and another net was stored on the net drum. Normally the seine net or the 'clean' trawl, for working smoother ground, was worked over the shelter. The heavy rockhopper trawl was worked from the net drum through a hatch in the transom.

The cod end of trawl or seine net was lifted by use of an A-frame derrick and Norlau gilson winch and emptied through the hydraulically operated bag hatch set into the starboard side of the shelter abaft the wheelhouse.

From the reception pound below the bag hatch the fish passed onto the variable speed conveyor which made catch handling quicker and easier and enhanced its quality by reducing the amount of necessary handling.

It got rid of the laborious task of scooping fish off the deck and shifting them forward and, as a crew member remarked, 'It saves the back'.

The crewmen could stand to gut the fish at the conveyor which was made of steel and nylon and extended along the starboard side to the vicinity of the fishroom hatch. Two fish washers were fitted forward of the casing.

Below the main deck, layout was conventional with fishroom followed by engineroom and cabin.

Some 1,400 boxes of fish could be carried in the fishroom which was cooled by a Sabroe chilling plant and insulated throughout with foam and fitted with aluminium stanchions and pound boards.

Callesen engine.

Sundari was powered by a Callesen 427-FOT six cylinder engine of 690hp at 425rpm, with integral gearbox and controllable pitch propeller.

Hydraulic pumps for the gear handling machinery were driven from the fore end through a Hytek gearbox. Each of two Volvo Penta 125hp auxiliary engines was coupled to a 220V alternator. Engineroom layout was uncluttered, and electrically driven fittings included two Desmi bilge and general service pumps and the chilling plant compressor.

An electro-hydraulic pump for bag hatch, transom hatch, conveyor, landing winch and windlass was fitted in the gear store forward. In all *Sundari* had seven fuel tanks holding in total some 7,000 gallons. Around 1,500 gallons of fresh water were carried below the fishroom.

The casing accommodated galley and messdeck, shower, washbasin and lavatory, and skipper's cabin, all with the restful decor and good quality finish associated with boats from Kristensen.

Galley facilities included Beha electric cooker, a fridge and deep freezer and a coffee maker.

Eight bunks were arranged in the after cabin.

Wide range of electronic instruments.

Furuno (UK) supplied FCV121 and FCV201 colour echosounders, FR801D Bright Track and FCR 1401 colour radars and GD2000 colour video plotter with Navstar 601D Navigator.

Using eight colours the FCV121 sounder could display echoes from the sounding frequencies of 28kHz and 200kHz simultaneously. It could show the entire water depth or bottom locked and pelagic expansions of 5, 10, 20, 40 or 80 metres and had echo storage facilities. Normal soundings or bottom locked expansions from 2.5 to 40 metres were displayed by the FCV201 50kHz sounder.

The three frequencies provided maximum discrimination in all water depths, 50kHz giving a good overall view whereas 28kHz was best for deep water and 200 for shallow water sounding.

The plotter/navigator set-up was one of a range of sophisticated micro-processor based navigation and track plotting systems becoming available in the early 1980s.

Interfaced with the Navstar navigator the GD2000 was a video plotter control unit which enabled navigation information to be overlaid with the radar picture on the FCR1401 screen so that the maximum amount of information was available on the one display. Various colours were used for plotting in a latitude and longitude grid and there was a choice of map scales.

The boat's current position was shown as a flashing dot and her track was recorded as she steamed or fished. Using a curser or control the location of the dahn could be marked graphically on the screen as a 'waypoint', enabling the skipper to steer back to the dahn. Other useful information such as the whereabouts of wrecks and rough ground could be entered onto the screen.

The picture could be stored on tape and recalled onto the screen to allow successful tows to be repeated. Furuno had already supplied some fifty sets to Scottish vessels at the time of *Sundari*'s completion.

Gurgly Gook.

Communications equipment included Skanti TRP8250 radiotelephone, and Sailor RT2047 VHF radiotelephone with CRY2001 Scrambler. Used with the radiotelephone for private conversations the scrambler produced a meaningless noise to outsiders. As one fisherman put it, 'It goes all gurgly gook'.

The scrambler and TR2047 radiotelephone came from the new range of compact radios from S. P. Sailor.

Favourable reactions.

Skippers reacted very favourably to a new 87ft design which Campbeltown Shipyard introduced in the 1980s.

Beamier, deeper and fuller in hull form than the yard's popular series of 85ft boats it would have substantially greater fuel and catch carrying capacities and yet should be as economical to operate.

Campbeltown decided to develop the larger design because of the increased top weight which Scottish vessels were carrying in the form of extra gear handling machinery, shelterdecks and the like. It would also enable longer-distance trips to be economically more worthwhile.

In 1984 Skipper Andrew Bremner and his Campbeltown-built 85ft *Boy Andrew* WK171 had opened up the Rockall fishing for seine net vessels. These lucrative grounds would provide a valuable alternative for the seine net fleet when North Sea fishing was slack, and an 87-footer could stay there longer and fetch back bigger catches, being able to hold more than 1,600 boxes compared with 1,300 carried by the 85-footers.

Main builder.

Campbeltown Shipyard had become the main builder of steel fishing boats in Britain having produced sixty-three by the start of 1985, the majority for Scottish owners. These included twenty cruiser sterned 80-footers and nine cruiser sterned 85-footers, and nine or ten with transom sterns.

By now Campbeltown was using Computer Aided Design techniques whereby skipper and designer could work out the general arrangement of a proposed new vessel within a day. Different layouts could be produced quickly on the computer screen for perusal and discussion, whereas formerly a skipper might have to visit the yard on several occasions while drawings were rubbed out and altered.

Andromeda II.

Campbeltown's first 87-footer for Scottish owners was the seiner trawler *Andromeda II* INS177 delivered to Skipper Angus Davidson of Hopeman late in 1985.

Skipper William Campbell MBE who had worked with Campbeltown on the 80- and 85-footers liaised closely with builders and Skipper Davidson in planning *Andromeda II*'s outline specification and layout and choosing her machinery, the aim being to increase safety and efficiency and where possible make her crew's work easier. Grampian Sea Fishing, of which Skipper Campbell was now Director, owned shares in the vessel.

Having transom stern and round bilges and full length non-weathertight steel and aluminium shelterdeck she measured 87.51ft overall with beam of 24.60ft and moulded depth of 13.94ft and Part IV tonnage of 108.38.

Gear and catch handling areas were separate and the casing offset to port. The main deck was divided into an after section housing rope reels and net bins, whereas

Andromeda II INS177 *in Peterhead's busy harbour.*
She was the first of the 'Campbeltown 87' class of seiner trawlers.
Note the hatch through which her nets were worked.

the forward section was arranged for fish reception and handling.

The seine net winch was on the shelterdeck abaft the wheelhouse and power block further aft. Ropes were worked over the shelter, travelling to and from the reels via small hatches in the shelter top.

Nets were shot and hauled from below the shelter through hydraulically operated hatches in the transom.

No-one need be on the shelter top except when retrieving the dahn and working the power block to haul aboard the net and swing the cod end round to the bag hatch which was set into the starboard side of the shelter adjacent to the wheelhouse. In bad weather the power block could be controlled from below the shelter.

When I visited her in 1987 *Andromeda II* had made seine netting trips in the North Sea of up to ten days duration and 240 miles from Peterhead, catching mainly cod, haddock and whiting. She had never lost a day's fishing through bad weather, being able to carry on working while other boats were 'dodging' the rough seas.

Pair seining.

Andromeda II was also one of dozens of Scots who were pair seining in summer in order to boost catches when fish was scarce. They used a large high net which could be kept open longer, and each boat used less fuel.

In 1988 she was pair trawling and pair seining in company with *Liberty* INS153. They had a reputation for quality fish and made record earnings for pair teams. They combined the two methods and could switch over from haul to haul as conditions dictated. Trawling caught more cod whereas seining on smooth ground yielded more haddock.

Andromeda II carried a single drum pair-trawl winch on the main deck foward.

She was powered by an air starting Callesen 575hp engine with controllable pitch propeller. It was chosen for its economical use of fuel, and by steaming at full engine revolutions, but cutting back on propeller pitch, she could save about three gallons of fuel an hour. Some 4,400 gallons of fuel were carried.

Swivelled.

Campbeltown offered the 87ft design with cruiser or transom stern and a choice of layouts.

Skipper Andrew Bremner chose a cruiser stern for his seiner trawler *Boy Andrew* WK170 built in 1986, as he considered it gave better towing and hauling capabilities.

Boy Andrew's seine winch and rope reels were on the main deck forward and split trawl winches, power block crane and net drum on the shelterdeck abaft the wheelhouse.

She had a sophisticated fish handling and conveyor system from Machinefabriek Van Rijn of Holland. It made fish gutting quick and simple and far less arduous. Her casing was offset to port and the handling system arranged along the starboard side from bag hatch to fishroom hatch.

Boy Andrew also had a special Becker rudder incorporating a tail piece which swivelled further to give a tighter turning circle and greater turning speed.

England.

In 1988 Campbeltown built its first boat for England the 87ft transom sterned *Maggie M*, MBE SH170 for Skipper Robert Mainprize of Scarborough. Her owners chose a steel boat as the gribble worms in Scarborough harbour would leave her alone.

From scratch.

James N. Miller and Sons Ltd. at St. Monans started building steel boats in the early 1980s following a £¼ million re-build of the yard which enabled it to offer wooden and steel vessels to its own or outside designs.

Men skilled in steel shipbuilding techniques were recruited from Clyde and Fife shipyards, but the firm continued to maintain the high standard of wooden boatbuilding for which it had been known for more than two hundred years.

Since the mid 1970s Miller had fitted out steel hulls built by McTay Marine Ltd. on Merseyside and was taken over by that firm in 1976.

The first steel boat built from scratch by Miller was the 60ft transom sterned *Oruna* BA20 for west coast owners in 1983. Designed by the Napier Co. she was one of the stoutest below-16.5m registered length boats to be built at that time. She has worked at Rockall and Skipper Iain Anderson said 'We fish regularly alongside 110-footers with exactly the same gear but we catch more fish'. Miller began to build steel vessels to its own design starting with the cruiser sterned seiner *Inter Nos II* KY57 delivered to Skipper William Smith in 1985.

With round bilges and raked soft nose stem she measured 85ft x 24ft 1in x 12ft 10in moulded depth. She was followed by the seiner trawlers *Solan* INS112 and *Vestrfjordr* K274 in 1985 and 1986 respectively.

Bigger ones.

In response to requests from fishermen the yard introduced a versatile 87ft design with high carrying capacities and sea range.

With cruiser or transom stern it could accommodate numerous configurations of casings and a wide choice of engine and deck machinery weights. It had the same hull design and beam as the 85-footers with extra length abaft the rudder post, providing more working space aft, and another foot in the fishroom, increasing fish carrying capacity by a hundred boxes.

The first 87-footer was the cruiser sterned seiner *Denebula* ME50, the largest fishing vessel ever built by Miller since its founding in 1747 but not the longest. During the nineteenth century the yard produced steam line boats and trawlers up to 90ft, but their beam was only 19ft x 20ft.

Denebula ME50 was the first 87ft steel boat from James N. Miller and Sons. She had a cruiser stern and was arranged primarily for seine netting. Her bag hatches were set port and starboard abaft the wheelhouse.

Built in 1986 for Skipper Michael Park of Inverbervie *Denebula* measured 87.38ft x 24ft 1in x 12ft 10in moulded depth and carried three-quarter-length non weathertight shelterdeck. Skipper Park had an early enthusiasm for fishing and at the age of ten was part owner of a creel boat.

Although *Denebula* was less roomy aft than a transom sterned boat her cruiser stern formed a half circle at deck level. Her casing and wheelhouse were set on the centreline and layout followed seiner pattern with winch and rope reels forward and power block and crane on the shelter aft. Ropes were worked over the shelter and bag hatches were set port and starboard in the shelter top abaft the wheelhouse.

Denebula could carry 1,800 boxes of fish and 6,600 gallons of fuel oil and was powered by a Mirrlees Blackstone ESL5 Mk 2 engine providing 680hp at 750rpm.

On trials she achieved a full speed of 11.5 knots using eleven gallons of fuel per hour. At 660rpm she did 10.5 knots, but showed a forty-five per cent drop in fuel consumption.

Her hull above the waterline, and the steel super-structure were shot blasted and hot zinc sprayed by Corrosion Control Ltd. The treatment formed a protective rust-retardent alloy skin on the metal and gave Cathodic protection. By now it was used on all Miller's steel hulled boats. The process involved shooting zinc wire through a gun. Propane gas in the gun melted the zinc and caused a spray of molten metal. This was sprayed over the plating which had previously been shotblasted to remove scale. Primer and an epoxy paint system was then applied.

The first.

Early in 1987 McCrindle Shipbuilding Ltd. of Ardrossan

in Ayrshire built its first fishing boat, the 80ft steel seiner trawler *Steadfast III* KY170 for Skipper Alec Gardner of Anstruther. Skipper Gardner had owned the wooden hulled *Steadfast* KY170 built at Peterhead by Irvins in 1969.

She was lost following an unfortunate encounter with an oil rig tender when fishing on the Ekofisk oil field in 1982. With her bow smashed she sank within six or seven minutes of the collision but happily the fishermen were safely picked up by the tender.

Subsequently Skipper Gardner fished for a while with a secondhand steel 80-footer before ordering *Steadfast III*.

Little prefabrication.

Coming from traditional Clydeside steel shipbuilding backgrounds McCrindle's workforce had worked on offshore oil projects which demanded high standards of plating and welding, and used these skills to good effect when building *Steadfast III*.

There are several ways of building steel vessels. *Steadfast III* was built like a wooden boat starting with the keel, and there was little prefabrication.

Mr. McCrindle told me that the yard set out to produce a quality good-looking boat. He said 'She has form, grace, shape and personality'.

Her cruiser stern was more pointed and her floors had more deadrise than many steel vessels and were slightly hollow. She had a fine entry, but her beam was carried from the flared shoulders to the quarters for fullness and ample working space.

A yacht designer planned her accommodation and decor, using restful greys and blues and various textures. Fresh air ventilation ducting prevented condensation in the accommodation.

With lines designed by S. C. McAllister *Steadfast III* measured near on 80ft overall with stout beam of some 24ft and depth of 13ft 5in. Wheelhouse and three-quarter-length non weathertight shelterdeck were aluminium.

Her hull was given a six-layer paint system fifty per cent thicker than normal.

Skipper Gardner was a top seine net fisherman and was by now a shareholder in Aberdeen Inshore Fishselling Co.

Steadfast III was primarily rigged for seining but had facilities for trawling. Split trawl winches tight forward on the main deck had their guiding-on gear on top for working wires over the shelter.

The seine winch was on the centreline followed by two rope reels set either side of the fishroom hatch. Ropes were worked over the shelter and the fixed cage-type hauling rollers had a shooting sheave above.

Casing and wheelhouse were on the centreline and bag hatches set in the shelter port and starboard aft.

Steadfast III made trips of some twelve days duration as compared with five or six worked by the wooden *Steadfast*.

Her technical specification shows the advances in equipment which had taken place since the first *Steadfast* and her sister ship *Forthright* were built eighteen years earlier

Steadfast III KY170

Technical specification.

Constructed of Lloyds Grade 'A' steel. Wheelhouse and shelterdeck marine grade aluminium.

Length overall	- 24.360 metres
Beam	- 7.250 metres
Depth	- 4.080 metres
Speed	- 10.6 knots
Fuel capacity	- 20,000 litres
Water capacity	- 5,000 litres
Fishroom capacity	- 980 boxes

Main engine. Kelvin TGSC8 - 650hp at 1350 rpm, driving the propeller through a Reintjes WAV500A 4:1 reduction gearbox. Front end gearbox — Kumera-Norgear type 4FGC-280, driving Voith 1PH6/6125/125 hydraulic pump for seine and trawl winches, and gilson winches, and Vickers 2520V hydraulic pump for other equipment.

There were tremendous developments in electronic equipment in the 1980s.
Steadfast III *KY170 had about twenty separate navigation, communications and fishfinding instruments in her wheelhouse.*

Auxiliary engines.

Volvo TD 100CHC 215hp at 1500rpm, driving a Stamford 40kW 415V alternator, a Transmotor ACG156 24V alternator, a Voith 1PH6/6125/125 hydraulic pump and Vickers 2520V hydraulic pump. Volvo D70 CHC 84hp at 1500rpm, driving Stamford 40kW 415V alternator, Transmotor ACG156 24V alternator and Desmi SA80/220/17 bilge and general service pump.

One Desmi electrically driven pump.

Hydraulic equipment (Fishing Hydraulics).

Seine net winch type SNW810 with 3.9 ton pull.
Split trawl winches type TWS705/9592, each 10 ton pull.
Rope reels 26 coils of 3½in diameter rope each.
Two gilson winches type M10.

One landing winch type FH124/A.
Atlas short post crane with 24RA power block.
Main hydraulic system driven from Volvo TD 100CHC engine through Automative Products clutch, with full backup from main engine step up gearbox.

Steering — Tenfjord H330-130TC-ESG.

Engine controls and alarm panels — Newbury.

Fire and Halon gas system — Chubb Marine.

Electronic equipment.

Communications — Sailor T2031/R2022 radiotelephone, RT2047 VHF radiotelephone, two RT144C radiotelephones, R501 watchkeeper and CRY scrambler; two Skanti TRP6000 radiotelephones and DS6001 scrambler; Yaesu FRG-8800 VHF receiver and Woodsons talk-back system.

Navigation — Decca RM770 and 970 radars, Mk21 and Mk53 Navigators and CVP3500 colour video plotter, Navstar 603S Transit Satelite navigator and Robertson AP40 autopilot with WA9 watch alarm.

Fishfinders — Skipper CS115 and CS116 colour echosounders.

Other wheelhouse fittings — E Vejvad Hansen chair, Ibuki horn, Wynstruments window wiper, Locat SRC-1 seine rope coil counter, Enviro Systems Fuel Stretcher, C. C. Jensen windows, three monitors for CCTV system, Skipper Taiyo FAX weather chart facsimile receiver.

Accommodation.

Linings — Capeboard marine panels.
Beha cooker, Candy fridge/deep freezer.
W.C., two washbasins, shower room.
Eight bunks in after cabin.
Flakt ventilation system.

Fishroom.

Insulation — foam pumped behind birch ply lining. Aluminium pound boards. Seacool 14-plate chilling system.

Other.

K.E.W. pressure deck washdown unit.
Two Balcomie fish washers.
Chalmit deck lights.
Fairleads and rollers — British Electrometals.

Chapter 7
TROUBLESOME YEARS:
FISHERMEN SEEK NEW OPPORTUNITIES

Moving towards the 1990s.

The 1980s had seen tremendous growth in the Scottish fishing industry, with heavy investment in new boats, but things became increasingly difficult as the decade drew to a close.

Further legislation was introduced in order to control fishing effort and ensure the survival of fish stocks.

On scientific advice there were reductions in quotas particularly for the main North Sea demersal species such as cod and haddock. There were also moves to reduce the number of boats in the fleet, in line with the European Multi-Annual Guidance Programme targets.

Grants for new boats became difficult to obtain. In 1988 grant priority was given to the replacement of lost vessels or those over fifteen years old which were withdrawn from fishing. In 1990 grant approval had to come from the EC before an SFIA grant could be given, but this scheme ended in 1991. Some grants continued to be paid in respect of approvals given under earlier schemes.

A number of boats were built privately with loans from financial institutions some of which set up schemes specially geared towards helping the fishermen. Others were built through the Government's Business Expansion Scheme.

A capacity aggregation scheme introduced in 1990 allowed a skipper to build a larger boat of up to 90 per cent of the capacity of two or more licensed ones which had been removed from the fleet. The 90 per cent figure was based on a formula involving dimensions and engine power and the first boat ordered under the scheme was a 'Campbeltown 87' which replaced two smaller vessels.

A drop in earnings.

At the start of the 1990s Scotland was still providing some 70 per cent of the total weight and 60 per cent of the total value of United Kingdom fish landings. In 1990 British boats put ashore some 460,000 tonnes worth almost £268 million in Scottish ports.

Although quayside prices for prime species remained generally high there was a drop in the fleet's gross earnings as the volume of landings began to decline and prices weaken. Difficulties were compounded by an increase in fuel costs.

Survival strategies.

But fishermen want their industry to survive and are looking at the issues of stock depletion and fleet over-capacity.

By the early 1990s they were having intense dialogue with fisheries ministers regarding effective conservation measures. Fishermen argued that the quota system did not work as it resulted in dumping fish at sea and the inducement to bypass the auction markets and sell 'over quota' catches illegally.

The fishermen protested vigorously against the Government's policy to limit the number of days fishing boats may go to sea.

In 1993 the fishermen's representatives presented ministers with alternative conservation proposals including the use of more selective trawl and seine nets which allow undersize fish to escape safely while retaining the greatest amount of marketable catch.

Seeking new opportunities.

The design of boats built during the late 1980s and early '90s reflected the fishermen's need to reduce their dependence on the traditional pressure stock fish and seek new grounds and catching opportunities.

Some skippers took a serious look at deepwater trawling to the west of Scotland with an emphasis on high value ground species such as megrims and monkfish.

One or two boats were near on 90ft long with capacity

to go even further afield should possibilities arise elsewhere.

Others used the twin-trawl, designed to catch prawns and flatfish and one or two east coast skippers moved from the seiner trawler class of vessel and bought smaller static gear boats. There was a growing interest in creel fishing because of European demand for shellfish previously discarded, such as velvet crabs.

Refinements.

During the late 1980s there were greater refinements in shelterdeck design and further thought given to the separation of fish and gear handling areas.

Fish handling systems became increasingly mechanised and gutting machines came back into favour.

The first wooden hulled boat designed and built with a full length shelterdeck was the transom sterned seiner trawler *Eleanda* BCK60 delivered from Herd and Mackenzie to Skipper David Main in 1988. She was the first of a new design, bigger generally all round with fuller lines and able to accommodate more powerful engine and heavier top weights.

With Part IV tonnage of 59.48 she measured 75ft 6in x 23ft 5in x 12ft. Skipper Main was very safety-conscious and her non-weathertight shelter had solid bulwarks on top at quarters and transom. Deck layout enabled seine and trawl gear to be separate. Two split trawl winches were sited port and starboard on main deck level at the quarters with warps travelling up through the shelter to blocks on the gantry. A net drum was offset to port abaft the winches. Seine winch and rope reels were well forward. Ropes were worked over the shelter via pendulum type hauling and shooting rollers set in openings in the after end of the bulwark atop the shelter.

Nets were shot and hauled aboard through hatches in the shelterdeck transom.

The bag hatch was set to starboard well aft in the shelter top. On main deck level the casing was offset to port to leave ample space for a fish handling system incorporating conveyors and fish washer made by B. & M. Engineering of Fraserburgh which had already supplied equipment to fifteen or sixteen Scottish boats.

Aboard *Eleanda* an elevator lifted the fish from the hopper beneath the bag hatch onto a conveyor belt running forward along the starboard side of the main deck. Crewmen gutted the fish on the conveyor and placed them in a trough alongside, where running water carried them forward to the fish washer.

Offal was thrown into another trough which carried it out through the boat's side.

Fish were lifted from the washer by another elevator and passed down a chute to the fishroom.

Eleanda was powered by a Kelvin 650hp TGSC8 engine. Thistle Marine supplied her deck machinery which was driven via hydraulic pumps from the Kelvin Seabird 225hp auxiliary engine.

Her wheelhouse was beautifully finished in a walnut laminate with mahogany trimmings and there were curtains at the windows. Most of the electronic equipment was set into consoles above and below the windows and included Sumar and Kaijo Denki echosounders and Wesmar sonar.

Shifted.

Macduff Boatbuilding built its first boat with full-length shelter the 67ft wooden-hulled trawler *Tranquillity* BF7 later in 1988 for Skipper Alex Ross.

Deck layout was unusual. The shape of her full width casing was staggered so that the port section was shifted further forward onto the port foredeck. This meant that the after bulkhead of the port section was also further forward leaving space for a net drum to be tucked in abaft it nearly 20ft forward of the transom, leaving ample room for net mending.

The starboard net drum was further aft and nets were worked through hatches in the transom.

Tranquillity's split trawl winches were on the shelterdeck abaft the wheelhouse so that the main deck forward was free for use of the B. & M. Engineering catch handling system.

The reception hopper below the bag hatch set to starboard forward had baffle plates and a grid to prevent boulders and debris from damaging the catch.

First full shelterdeck from Forbes.

J. and G. Forbes constructed its first boat with full length shelterdeck the 74ft x 23ft wooden-hulled *Sharona II* LH250 in 1989.

Skippered by Peter Moodie she was the fourth vessel built by Forbes for the successful Moodie family of Longniddry near the Firth of Forth, starting in 1983 with *Rose of Sharon III* LH56 followed by *Shemarah* LH65 in 1985 and *Sharon Rose III* LH119 in 1987.

Although the Moodies had been expert seine net fishermen they had turned increasingly towards trawling so *Sharona II* was equipped solely as a trawler although she could be fitted for seining if required.

Her shelter was weathertight to the end of the deckhouse and Rapp split winches were mounted atop the shelter abaft the wheelhouse.

Sharona II was powered by a Deutz 720hp engine turning a Bruntons five bladed fixed pitch propeller through a 5:1 reduction gearbox. Five bladed propellers could have smaller diameter providing better performance and less water noise.

Electronic instruments included C-Tech Omni Sonar CAS-36 from Krupp-Atlas Elektronik. A growing number of skippers were using this sonar for its excellent seabed interpretation which was invaluable when locating new fishing grounds.

Tranquillity replaced a below-16.5m boat of the same name and registration number, built by Macduff in 1983.

Skipper William Lawson of Peterhead also moved to a larger boat in 1988. His 75ft wooden-hulled transom sterned *Rosebay III* PD65, built by Gerrard Brothers, was much bigger than his previous command the 56ft *Rosebay* PD313, with which he had fished the inshore waters off Peterhead.

With *Rosebay III* he was able to work the more distant grounds where general fish scarcity was forcing the Scottish fleet to go.

Twin trawls.

She was also equipped to handle twin trawls.

This gear comprises two identical trawls towed side by side using three warps worked from a triple drum winch. A heavy weight or roller on the central warp keeps the gear on the bottom.

Developed in Denmark it is suitable for catching species such as prawns, shrimps and flatfish which live tight to the seabed, and where gear spread is more important than headline height.

Two nets are better than a bigger single net because greater width is obtained without a relative increase in drag, and smaller nets are easier to handle.

Prawns, correctly named Nephrops Norvegicus, are the most valuable shellfish species in Scotland. Inshore trawlers have enjoyed a big fishery in the Moray Firth and Firth of Forth areas.

Twin rig gear could also be used for catching flat and round fish on the more distant grounds.

Scottish skippers began to use the gear in the 1980s and as the decade progressed the prawn fishery helped to augment dwindling earnings from the traditional pressure stock species.

In 1987 Gerrard Brothers delivered the stout little 50ft wooden-hulled trawler *E'phraim* FR3 to Skipper Michael Watt. Especially equipped for twin rig trawling she carried Rapp three-drum winch on the main deck forward and the twin trawls were carried on a split net drum at the quarters.

E'phraim tried the gear at the prawn fishery late in 1987 and out-fished the other boats by some fifty per cent, which more than compensated for the slight increase in fuel consumption. The gear also caught more demersal fish than the single trawl.

Three towing blocks.

In order to improve manoeuvrability and towing

Rosebay III PD65 in Peterhead's busy harbour.
Her casing was offset to starboard below the shelterdeck rather than in the more usual position to port.

power while towing twin trawls, Fishing Hydraulics supplied *Rosebay III* with a Scansea hydraulic towing gantry carrying three hanging blocks. Using remote controls in the wheelhouse these were moved along the gantry into the most effective position. The Scansea triple drum winch was mounted on main deck forward with the guiding-on gear angled upwards to work the warps over the shelterdeck. A system of sheaves directed the warps to the hanging blocks, one warp passing the wheelhouse on one side and two the other before coming together at the gantry which spanned the after end of the shelterdeck.

A Scansea split net drum on the quarters could hold twin trawls or a big pair trawl.

Offset to starboard.

Rosebay III had other offbeat features. Her steel casing containing the main deck accommodation was offset to starboard leaving a passageway along the port side linking afterdeck and foredeck. The boat naturally tended to list to starboard when taking fish aboard but with the passageway placed along the port side there would be little chance of water swilling around in it.

Measuring 74.8ft with 22.63ft beam and 10ft moulded depth *Rosebay III* was designed by S. C. McAllister and carried her beam for much of her length, but her reasonably fine waterline entry forward gave her a good speed of around eleven knots.

The three-quarter-length weathertight shelterdeck was aluminium with the bag hatch position to starboard in the shelter top forward of the wheelhouse.

The large reception hopper had a separate section for shrimps. The fish handling system incorporated a gutting conveyor running athwartships forward of the casing.

Gutting machines.

Shortly after her completion *Rosebay III* was fitted with two Kronborg gutting machines which would cut down manual work further and enabled her to sail with a crew of only five.

Gutting machines were coming back into favour as they speeded up the handling process and enabled fish to be put in the fishroom quickly, with beneficial effects on quality.

Rosebay III used Pers plastic fish boxes which held eight or nine stone and could be stacked without squashing the contents, and enhanced her carrying capacity. Holding some 1,200 boxes the fishroom was equipped with a Fishcool steel plate chilling plant from Forbes Refrigeration.

She had a Caterpillar 705hp propulsion engine with Teignbridge 73 in fixed pitch propeller.

The Linde and Vickers hydraulic pumps for her deck machinery were driven from the Volvo 215hp auxiliary engine. Wheelhouse fittings included a Krupp Atlas Fischfinder 722 combined colour and paper sounder and a Scanmar 4003 net monitor.

Sensors on the net indicated headline height and the quantity of fish in the cod end.

A notice in the wheelhouse said 'Nobody's perfect except the Captain'.

The middle warp.

Other boats used different ways of dealing with the middle warp when twin trawling.

On the 65ft steel trawler *Celnius II* BCK151 it travelled in a straight line beneath the wheelhouse floor to the towing gantry thereby eliminating the need for a complex system of guides and rollers.

Celnius II was built in 1988 by James N. Miller for Skipper Willie Mair. Her net drum was offset to port on the after end of her three-quarter-length shelter and power block crane to starboard. This left the afterdeck clear for handling and mending the large nets used for working clean ground. The clean nets would be hauled by the power block whereas the net drum would be used for handling rockhopper nets or twin trawls.

A three-drum trawl winch was situated on main deck forward, and the Deutz 554hp engine turned the fixed pitch propeller in a Kort nozzle.

Around this time, Millers erected a shed at Methil docks. This created a covered wet dock into which boats were floated for fitting out so that work was not held up by bad weather.

Millers was by now very versatile, having built a range of steel boats including a 60ft crabber for Teignmouth and an 88ft longliner for Milford Haven, and several 87ft trawlers and seiner trawlers for Scottish owners.

The yard was now a member of a big engineering

Celnius II BCK151 was equipped for working single and twin trawls. Note her net drum on the after end of her shelterdeck with the power block to starboard.

group John Mowlem which had taken over Miller's parent company McTay Marine.

Further steps forward.

Further steps forward in Miller's 87ft design were incorporated into the seiner trawler *Carvida* FR457 delivered to Skipper Andrew Buchan in 1988. Costing around £1 million to build she was the forerunner in layout for five vessels built by Miller during the subsequent two years.

The casing spanned her width leaving a passageway to starboard linking fore and after decks and giving access into the deckhouse. Skipper Buchan formerly owned the 87ft wooden-hulled *Carvida* FR347 with which he concentrated on seining. Owing to the scarcity and distribution of fish in the late 1980s he began trawling with the new *Carvida*, making trips of ten to twelve days.

Her full length shelter was aluminium but with whale-back and after section steel, and was weathertight forward of the deckhouse.

Two Rapp split trawl winches each holding 700 fathoms of 22mm wire were set atop the shelter abaft the wheelhouse and angled outwards to run the warps directly through towing blocks hung from post-type gallows.

The power block and crane were on the centreline abaft the winches. On main deck level two net drums were set abaft the casing, leaving a huge amount of space for net mending.

Three nets, one on each drum and another in a bin, could be ready for working as required. They were worked through hatches in the transom in line with the net drums. Trawl doors were stowed in recesses in the shelterdeck below the gallows.

The seine winch lay on the shelterdeck abaft the foremast and two rope reels were set forward on the main deck. Ropes were worked over the shelter.

The hydraulic bag hatch was located to starboard in the shelter top forward of amidships.

Fish were gutted at a conveyor running athwartships forward of the casing and the Seacool fishroom cooling plant used eighteen non-eutectic plates.

Carvida was powered by a Mirrlees Blackstone ESL5 Mk 2 830hp engine at 750rpm turning an Ulstein controllable pitch propeller through a 2.54:1 reduction gearbox.

A hydraulic pump driven from the main engine powered a 415V alternator. This supplied a constant output regardless of changes in engine revolutions and saved fuel as AC current could be supplied without the need to run the auxiliary engine.

Fixed delivery hydraulic pumps for the deck machinery were driven from the Gardner 310hp auxiliary engine.

Carvida's huge array of electronic fittings included a Microplot computer system from Sea Information Systems Ltd. of Aberdeen. Basically it comprised a colour video plotter produced as software for use with a VDU and a printer. Capable of interfacing with any position finding equipment it could record the boat's track and receive and record information put in by the user, such as waypoints and seabed data.

It had a massive information storage facility.

Fish detectors included Chromascope CVS-886 Mk2 and Kaijo Denki echosounders and Scanmar 4003 catch monitor.

She carried a Rapp Hydema PTS-3000 Programmable Trawl System. A computer linked to the hydraulic system removed much of the guesswork from setting, towing and hauling the trawl. For instance, it payed out the required length of warp and adjusted pressure in order to maintain correct towing speed and compensate for changes in net configuration.

Intriguing.

One of the most intriguing developments of the late 1980s was the move by Macduff Boatbuilding into steel boats using a procedure new to Scottish yards but widely used in Holland.

Macduff designed the boat and sent lines plans to a Dutch steel cutting firm which did the lofting, cut and shaped the bars and plates and sent them in kit form to Macduff ready for building the vessel.

The Dutch have huge experience in this computer-aided lofting and cutting work.

The kit method gave Macduff control over constructing the hull without the need for costly steelworking machinery.

First steel boat.

The first steel boat the 60ft trawler *Heather Sprig* BCK181 was handed over to Skipper John Smith of Buckie in 1989. Coming below 16.5m registered length she was of similar principal dimensions and Part IV tonnage to her builder's wooden-hulled below-ticket boats, but the use of steel brought about some differences in hull shape. She had a larger propeller aperture and finer waterline entry and was also given a semi bulbous bow which cannot be created very satisfactorily in a wooden hull.

Heather Sprig was 61ft long with beam of 22ft 6in and extreme depth of 13ft 9in. Water ballast tanks under the fishroom could be filled or emptied to adjust trim.

Her athwartships deckhouse and non weathertight aluminium shelterdeck with weathertight forecastle were of similiar design to those of *Helenus*.

Twin trawls.

Heather Sprig's deck layout and gear handling equipment was planned for working twin trawls. A Jensen triple-drum trawl winch was positioned athwartship forward. All three warps travelled up through cowls in the shelter. The port and starboard warps were angled outwards via deck sheaves and passed either side of the wheelhouse to hanging blocks on the gantry which spanned the after end of the shelter.

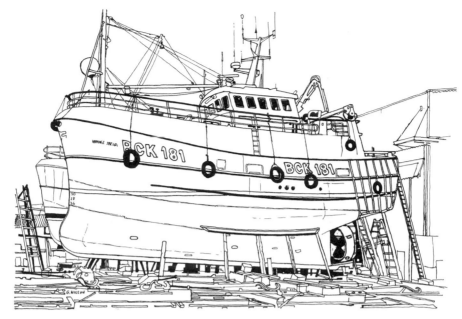

Heather Sprig BCK181 on the slipway at Macduff after a repaint.
She was the first steel boat built by the Macduff Boatbuilding and Engineering Co.
(now Macduff Shipyards).
Note her Kort nozzle and semi bulbous bow.

The middle warp had a straight run to a sheave mounted just forward of the wheelhouse and travelled through a channel under the wheelhouse floor and thence to a central block hung from the gantry. From the hanging blocks the warps ran through three Thistle Marine tension meter towing blocks hung from a sleeve fitted around a steel bar positioned between the uprights of the gantry. This sleeve slid freely along the bar to enable the gear to be towed from the best angle and gave *Heather Sprig* good manoeuvrability while towing.

Two Jensen net drums were mounted on the after-deck. They were driven on a common shaft but were clutched independently. Each drum had a dividing flange so that four nets could be carried ready for shooting as required.

Smoother run.

A Thistle Marine 24in power block was slung from a HAP crane offset slightly to starboard on the after end of the shelter.

Cod ends, two each time, were taken forward to the bag hatch fitted to starboard in the shelter top forward of the wheelhouse.

A Thistle gilson winch worked the traditional pole fish derrick which was stayed to the foremast.

The B. & M. conveyor in the fish handling area had a close link polyurethane belt specially designed for handling shrimps and prawns.

Forbes Refrigeration Ltd. of Ellon made the Fish-cool fishroom cooling system, using acid resistant stainless steel evaporators.

134

Kort nozzle.

Skipper Smith chose a Deutz propulsion engine for *Heather Sprig*. It was an SBA8M816R which developed 554hp at 1500rpm and drove through a Heimdal 5:1 reduction gearbox to a Heimdal controllable pitch propeller in a fixed Kort nozzle. Kort designed the nozzle to give the boat a reasonable increase in towing thrust together with good steaming characteristics.

On trials she had a free running speed of eleven knots and had an estimated bollard pull of eight tonnes. She carried 14½ tonnes of fuel oil.

Heather Sprig also carried an item unusual in so small a vessel, an Alfa-Laval separator which cleaned the fuel oil.

A Hamworthy variable delivery hydraulic pump for the winch and net drums and Vickers pump for the other deck units were driven from the main engine via a Norgear gearbox. Two Ford auxiliary engines each driving a 415V alternator were supplied by C-Power (Marine) Ltd.

In all *Heather Sprig* carried twenty electronic instruments. Fishfinders comprised Kaijo Denki Memo Colour 200 and JMC V-122 colour echosounders.

The Kaijo Denki could show a fishlupe alongside the normal recording for differentiation between bottom feeding fish and the seabed. Another option offered detailed scrutiny of a particular echo, to see if it was all fish, partly fish or just feeding stuffs.

Navigation instruments included a Shipmate RS4000 CC Navigator. A more advanced version of the RS4000C this had additional facilities including preparation for the future GPS or Global Positioning System. Using satellites, GPS provides continuous position fixing with a good degree of accuracy. GPS coverage of the North Sea was in operation by the start of the 1990s.

Various alarm sensors were placed around *Heather Sprig* so that unwanted intruders would set off a flashing light on the masthead and a siren in the wheelhouse and an alarm signal in the harbour office. Alarm systems for use when vessels were left tied up in port were now essential because of the enormous value of their equipment.

Bow thruster.

Jones Buckie Shipyard built its first steel vessel the 77ft trawler *Faithful* UL179 in 1988. Skipper Alan Phimister wanted a steel boat but with the Jones quality of finish.

Designed by S. C. McAllister she had stout 24ft beam, transom stern and full length non-weathertight shelter.

Her hull was built by the Yorkshire Dry Dock Co. To enhance manoeuvrability she had a bow thruster, unusual in this size and class of vessel but a standard feature in the purse seiner fleet. *Faithful*'s Rapp split trawl winches were atop the shelter aft.

A same-make net drum was set to starboard on the main deck adjacent to the fore end of the casing, giving near on 40ft of net mending space. Nets were hauled through a hatch in the transom.

Propulsion was provided by a Deutz 670hp engine driving through a Heimdal 5:1 reduction gearbox to a controllable pitch propeller in a Kort nozzle.

One of the two Deutz auxiliary engines provided power for the main hydraulic pumps for the deck machinery, while the smaller model drove the Bertel-O-steen bow thruster. The engine exhausts were contained in the sturdy trawl gallows aft rather than passing through the wheelhouse.

The B. & M. Engineering fish handling system included a gutting conveyor.

Absence of the engine exhaust trunking gave all-round vision from the wheelhouse. Electronics included three echosounders.

Inexhaustible.

Despite the interest in steel there were people who preferred wooden boats. In 1987 Alexander Noble and Sons Ltd. of Girvan in Ayrshire built the transom sterned pair trawler *Margarets* LH232 for Skipper David Fairnie.

A native of Fraserburgh, Alexander Noble founded his

yard in 1946 and has said 'Wood is such a kindly material to handle and can be worked into the most beautiful shapes. Providing man is wise and keeps planting and looking after his forests, wood is one of the few raw materials that is inexhaustible'.[6]

His boats are recognised for high standards of craftsmanship and finish. The majority were built for west coast owners and included in the earlier years some very beautiful canoe sterned ring netters.

At 69ft x 23ft with three-quarter-length shelter and Part IV tonnage of 61.83 *Margarets* is the yard's biggest boat to date. Gear handling machinery includes a three-drum winch to enable her to work the twin rig if need be.

[6]*The Scottish Inshore Fishing Vessel Design, Construction and Repair* by Alexander Noble. National Maritime Museum, Maritime Monographs and Reports. No 31-1978.

A welcome return.

Richard Dunston (Hessle) Ltd. made a return to the fishing boat market with the 86ft fully shelterdecked steel trawler *Veracious II* PD373 delivered in 1988 to Skipper John Forman of Peterhead.

A big full-lined boat with deep bilges and beam of 24.6ft and moulded depth of 13.6ft she was designed to fish more distant grounds such as Rockall, and to have greater flexibility as dictated by increasing quota limitations.

With transom stern and semi bulbous bow her hull was designed especially to accommodate her particular layout and machinery rather than being a standard shape.

She was primarily equipped for single and pair trawling with the option of seine netting, and showed herself to be a good seaboat.

Shore Hydraulics.

Nets were worked through hydraulically operated hatches in the shelter's after end.

All the deck machinery was supplied by Shore Hydraulics Ltd. of Peterhead, which had recently introduced a full range of rugged units designed to meet the demands of powerful boats and heavier fishing gear. Split trawl winches were situated on the shelter abaft the wheelhouse and were controlled manually or by an F. K. Smith Datatrawl automatic computer-based shooting, towing and hauling system.

Each winch could carry 600 fathoms of 24mm warp. Two net drums were on the quarters below the shelter, the starboard drum further forward to leave space for net repair.

An A-frame gallows on the centreline at the after end of the shelter enabled *Veracious II* to switch from single to pair trawling without danger of the single warp snagging on the trawl doors stowed at the quarters.

A Tico crane on the shelterdeck forward replaced the usual boom swinger and landing derrick. It enabled her to offload eight boxes each lift thereby reducing landing time.

Lighten the load.

Cod ends were lifted aboard through the bag hatch offset to starboard forward of the wheelhouse and emptied into a small receiving hopper. From here the catch was fed to a large hopper which spanned the centreline and enabled the fish to spread out and not be damaged by its own weight.

An elevator carried the fish to the handling area on main deck forward.

Designed to lighten the fishermen's workload the handling system was built by Anchor Services (Phd) Ltd. and incorporated a conveyor which automatically graded the fish according to size. Large fish were gutted by hand and smaller ones handled by one or other of two Kronborg gutting machines.

Skipper Forman put great emphasis on keeping the catch in good condition during longer trips and so the 1,475-box capacity fishroom was well insulated with injected polyurethane foam behind a lining of aluminium sheet on top of plywood, and fitted with a Seacool chilling system.

Veracious II was powered by a MAN B&W Alpha engine which developed 850hp at 825rpm and drove through an Alpha gearbox to a controllable pitch propeller which turned at 268rpm in a fixed nozzle. It gave her a free running speed of 11.4 knots.

The main hydraulic system was driven from the fore end of the engine through a Kumera Norgear gearbox, and a hydraulically powered Waterborne alternator was driven from the after end. Engine and sterngear were controlled by the Alphatronic system which automatically adjusted propeller pitch and engine revolutions to provide optimum efficiency.

A Volvo 215hp engine provided secondary power for the hydraulic and electrical system. *Veracious II* could carry some 6,000 gallons of fuel oil.

Electronic instruments were mainly of Woodsons and Racal Decca supply and included Kaijo Denki and JMC colour echosounders and CVP3500 plotter.

Dunstons delivered a sister ship, *Venture* PD72, to Skipper Forman's brother Michael in 1989.

She was similar to *Veracious II* in most respects. Small differences included a stout crossbar between the gallows, carrying a sheave for the pair-trawl warp.

A whopper.

Another whopper of a steel boat was the 91ft 6in x 26ft 10in seiner trawler *Auriga III* LH449 built in 1989 by Richards (Shipbuilders) Ltd. at Lowestoft for one of Scotland's most esteemed fishermen Skipper Jim Vanko.

She carried a huge amount of equipment.

Despite lack of grant assistance her owners decided to build her because a large adaptable boat would be competitive in the light of increasing limitations on British vessels.

Costing £1.6 million and fully equipped for seining and trawling she could work in the North Sea and at Rockall, and anywhere she would be licenced to fish in the future.

With transom stern and bulbous bow, and coming below 80ft registered length, *Auriga III* was designed to her skipper's requirements with optimum deck space and big carrying capacity. Her hull shape was designed to accommodate her particular layout and fittings. She had full lines with deep round bilges, and the fully bulbous bow enhanced her seakeeping and handling capabilities and produced greater speed.

Her full length shelterdeck was weathertight to the aft end of the casing.

Danish engine.

Supplied by Coastal Marine Eyemouth her Callesen 427 FTK-G six cylinder engine, rated at 900hp and 470rpm, turned the controllable pitch propeller through a 2:1 reduction gear. These Danish engines had become liked in Scotland for their simple construction, low fuel and oil consumption, long life and low maintenance costs.

Auriga III was the first in the UK to have a Becker steering nozzle with a small flap rudder attached to the rear of the nozzle. This increased her manoeuvrability and towing capabilities and gave better propulsive efficiency thereby saving fuel.

It also helped in her design by allowing her to have fuller lines amidships and aft without restricting water flow to the propeller and enabling her to be nearly 92ft long overall, yet below 80ft registered length.

Auriga III also had two 90hp Hundested side thrusters.

Multi sheave.

Her gear handling machinery included Oilpower split trawl winches on the shelterdeck abaft the wheelhouse and each having an 18 tonne heave at the core and holding 1200 fathoms of 20mm warp. They were controlled by an autotrawl system which incorporated a display screen showing warp performance.

Two net drums were carried, one on the shelter top and the other below.

An Oilpower multi sheave seine winch and three Fishing Hydraulics rope reels were well forward on the main deck.

Spanning the stern a hefty gantry carried seine and trawl towing rollers which could be moved hydraulically into any position across the stern.

The fish handling system, designed by Torry Research Station and Skipper Vanko and made by Anchor Services incorporated two Kronborg gutting machines.

Auriga III's 2,000-box capacity fishroom had a cooling system from Pitkin and Ruddock.

Some thirty electronic instruments were carried.

Using sensors on the net, a Scanmar colour graphics monitor displayed the geometry of the net and showed how rigging adjustments affected its performance.

Fishfinders included Krupp Atlas Echoscope 382 colour sounder and Elac colour sonar. A Furuno C1-30 doppler sonar current indicator displayed such things as the speed of the current at various depths, and the boat's movement in leeway, fore-aft and lateral directions, thereby giving the skipper useful information when setting the gear.

Her Furuno radar had a control panel which allowed overlay of course plotting and navigational information. Furuno also supplied a FAX-214 facsimile receiver which processed weather charts and satellite images transferred from FAX stations.

Other fittings included Racal Decca 350T Track Plotter and two CVP3500 video plotters, and Mk 53, Mk21 and MNS2000 navigators. Auriga III carried 9,240 gallons of fuel to give her good sea range.

Stepping down a notch.

Some skippers stepped down a notch.

After being in command of seiners around 80ft long, Skipper William Ritchie of Peterhead took delivery of the hefty little 55ft wooden hulled trawler *Headway IV* PD229 from Gerrard Brothers in 1990. She has fished on the Bergen Bank which is somewhat distant for such a small boat, but she also works the inshore grounds.

Designed by S. C. McAllister and measuring 54ft 10in by 21ft 2in with Part IV tonnage of 38.46 *Headway IV* had three-quarter-length non-weathertight shelterdeck. Powerful deck machinery from Shore Hydraulics included a big double net drum able to carry two sets of twin rig gear.

It comprised two drums on a centre pedestal so that one

drum could be replaced by a rope reel should *Headway IV* switch to pair seining. A three-drum trawl winch with 14 tonne pull was fitted forward and warps were worked over the shelter, the centre warp for the twin rig gear directed past the wheelhouse via guides and rollers to the towing gantry.

Headway IV was powered by a 365hp Caterpillar engine with 64in propeller and 6:1 reduction gearbox. She used a Chromascope colour echosounder.

Single rope reel.

A number of trawlers had the option of pair seining.

The 67ft wooden-hulled *Elegance* PD33 skippered by Robert Smith carried a single rope reel and single barrel seine winch. She was built in 1989 by Macduff Boatbuilding for Grimsby owners Tom Sleight Seiners, but worked from north-east Scotland.

Static gear.

In the light of falling stocks of white fish and the high costs of big boats some skippers moved from the seiner trawler class down to small static gear vessels.

In 1990 Skipper Sandy McLeod had the 39ft steel *Hazel Louise* INS70 built at Berwick by Coastal Marine Boatbuilders Ltd. of Eyemouth.

Rugged.

More skippers wanted boats suitable for working the Atlantic deep water fisheries in order to supplement decreasing earnings from traditional pressure stock species.

The 75ft steel hulled *Westro* INS20 built by Macduff in 1992 for Skipper Graham Thomson of Lossiemouth was enormously rugged with very full lines and broad beam of 25ft and moulded depth of 14ft 6ins. Her hull was extended up to shelterdeck level and her bulbous bow contained seawater ballast which could be pumped out to maintain trim at all times.

Her flared bow provided additional space forward on deck and below.

Powerful deck machinery from Fishing Hydraulics

enabled her to fish as deep as 400 fathoms. Each having a first-layer pull of 12.2 tonnes and designed to carry 1100 fathoms of 22mm wire, the two Rapp split trawl winches were on shelterdeck level abaft the aluminium wheelhouse. The extra wide ribbed sheave power block was affixed to an Outreach Loglift crane chosen for its strength. Two net drums were situated below the shelter aft. Nets were worked through transom hatches fitted with hydraulically driven rollers which helped to handle the heavy rockhopper trawls.

Westro was designed to work several types of trawl including semi-pelagic nets.

She was designed by Macduff and Skipper Thomson, and her hull constructed by the Yorkshire Dry Dock Co. Ltd. using plates and sections sent in kit form from Holland. The hull was towed to Macduff for completion.

A 26.75 tonne fuel carrying capacity gave her considerable sea range. Skipper Thomson planned to fish as far as Rockall and along the edge of the Continental Shelf and land at Lochinver.

Propulsion was provided by a Deutz MWM type TBD 604 BV8 engine of 642hp turning a Heimdal 75in diameter controllable pitch propeller in a Kort nozzle.

The 604B range of engines was designed for use in small enginerooms where compactness was important. Providing more power per cylinder than the 816 range it was economical on fuel and designed to accommodate changing loads and speeds.

The main hydraulic pumps were powered from the engine through a Hytek gearbox.

Westro's bag hatch was set to starboard forward and her fish handling system had a gutting conveyor and selection bins. Fitted with a Fishcool chilling plant the fishroom could easily carry a thousand boxes.

Electronics included Krupp Atlas 722 echosounder, Rapp PTS3000 trawl control system and Microplot Version 5 computer-based colour video plotter.

Supplied by Sea Information Systems of Aberdeen the Microplot used the RoxAnn facility which was ideal for use when locating and opening up new fishing grounds.

Linked to the echosounder transducer it gave an accurate indication of the nature of the seabed. Different types of sea bottom were shown as a range of colours along the boat's track on the plotter screen.

After ninety years.

Sadly, after ninety years in business, J. and G. Forbes launched its last large boat the 73ft x 22ft wooden-hulled seiner trawler *Fruitful Vine* BF240 in 1990 before closing down the Sandhaven premises and moving to a small repair yard in Fraserburgh.

Built for Skipper John Nicol of Gardenstown *Fruitful Vine* had a full length shelterdeck which was weathertight for three quarters of its length. Her 200-box capacity fish reception hopper was fitted athwartships across the foredeck so that she would not list when it was full.

The catch handling system enabled fish to be pre-selected on deck. Alongside the gutting conveyor there were six bins to take different sizes of gutted fish. Each bin had a capacity for one box of fish and when it was full a door was opened to allow the contents to pass to the washer and thence via a conveyor to the fishroom. This was the second system of its type to be supplied by B. & M. Engineering.

Fruitful Vine was powered by a Cummins KTA 19 M engine of 500hp at 1800rpm turning a Teignbridge 66in five bladed propeller through a 6:1 reduction gearbox. Specially designed for the boat the propeller produced little noise or vibration.

Using her Robertson three drum winch, *Fruitful Vine* could work twin trawls, the centre warp running aft beneath the wheelhouse. Alternatively she could carry seine rope on the third drum to enable her to switch quickly between pair trawling and pair seining.

Kept going.

Macduff Boatbuilding, now renamed Macduff Shipyards, has kept going.

In 1992 it built the 68ft x 22ft 6in wooden-hulled trawler *Andrianne* INS8 for forward-looking skipper

Sandy Patience of Avoch. He foresaw a future in fishing if skippers were ready to adjust to change and accept the value of conservation.

Andrianne was equipped for all trawling methods including twin rig and could also work deep water off the Scottish west coast. Skipper Patience planned to try white fish pelagic trawling which many Scots had not persevered with. Irish boats had worked the gear well so Skipper Patience bought his pelagic net and trawl doors from makers in Kilkeel.

On main deck level *Andrianne* carried Rapp three-drum trawl winch and two split net drums.

Her Deutz 560hp engine drove through a 5.59:1 reduction gear to the four bladed Bruntons propeller in a Kort nozzle to give increased towing thrust.

Deck machinery was driven from the Volvo 215hp auxiliary engine and other fittings included B. & M. fish handling conveyor and Fishcool chilling plant.

Instrumentation.

Andrianne was the first British white fish trawler to have a Simrad ITI Trawl Instrumentation system, of particular value for pelagic trawling.

Using cable-less sensors on the net it could give graphic information on net performance including door spread, headline height, water temperature, the distance and bearing of the trawl and its rate of ascending and descending, distance between footrope and seabed, and the quantity of fish in the cod end.

It could also show information from other instruments such as sonar or echosounder on the screen. This enabled the user to manoeuvre the boat so that the net would hit the fish indicated by the sonar or sounder.

Andrianne carried Simrad EQ50 sounder and Furuno CH16 sonar. One of the first installations anywhere in the world the EQ50 used ceramic tansducers and a high signal to noise ratio providing sharp fish detection and ground discrimination.

The wood used in building *Andrianne* came from the Yorkshire firm of Barchards Ltd. for many years a major supplier of boatbuilding timbers to yards throughout the UK and Ireland.

For around a hundred years there has been an interchange of skills and ideas between Scottish and English fishermen and boatbuilders. For example, early Scottish steam drifters came from English yards, and in the 1930s Scottish firms built motor fifies for Yorkshire skippers.

The tradition continues.

One of the most recent additions to the Scottish fleet the 59ft 6in x 21ft 7in steel twin-rig trawler *Sardonyx II* BF206 was delivered from Hepworth Shipyard at Paull near Hull to Scottish skipper Sandy Watt. She was one of a number of robust steel vessels built to various designs by Hepworth for the Scots fleet in recent years.

And in 1988 James N. Miller and Sons upheld its association with Whitby when it built the 60ft transom sterned steel trawler *Sophie Louise* WY168 for Skipper Howard Locker.

She is an example of Miller's ability to build vessels to skippers' individual requirements and was the first large newly-built steel boat to join the port's fleet of some twenty trawlers which were mostly 60ft and under to allow them to fish within three miles of certain parts of the local coastline.

Strong tides.

With length overall of 59.9ft and generous 22ft beam and moulded depth of over 12ft *Sophie Louise* is a robust boat arranged for side and stern trawling.

Skipper Locker finds that side fishing gives better manoeuvrability when working in strong tides and restricted bits of hard bottom where the gear might snag. Stern trawling is more suitable for longer tows with a bigger net over sandy bottom in deeper water. *Sophie Louise* has worked on the oil fields some 280 miles from Whitby and also at the Devil's Hole, some 150 miles from port, where she has caught a lot of monkfish. She is known by the fish merchants for landing top quality catches.

Sophie's aluminium shelterdeck which extends from stem to casing is offset to port leaving the starboard deck area clear for side trawling. The North Sea Winches trawl winch which carries 400 fathoms of $2\frac{1}{2}$in wire on each drum is offset to port forward with the warps passing through the shelter side to the gallows fitted to starboard.

A stout North Sea Winches net drum on the quarters is used for stern fishing and a Tico crane with a built-in winch on the casing top lifts the heavy hopper ground gear over the transom.

Cod ends are lifted aboard on the starboard side and swung into the reception pound through sliding doors in the shelterdeck. With capacity for 600 boxes, the fishroom has a Viking chilling system.

The 495hp Kelvin engine drives through a 4:1 reduction gearbox to an FAL propeller in a Kort nozzle, and also powers the main hydraulic pumps through a Norgear gearbox.

Wheelhouse fittings include Furuno CH14 sonar for ground discrimination and two Furuno FCV 261 echosounders one of which is interlinked with a net transducer to provide information about the fishing gear.

Closed down.

Skipper Locker is very pleased with *Sophie Louise*. He said 'Miller's have built some lovely boats. We would go anywhere in her. I'm sorry Miller's have closed down'.

After almost 250 years of fishing boat building, James N. Miller closed in 1992. Part of the John Mowlem group, the yard was shut down as part of a rationalisation programme, and any future orders would go to the group's other yard, McTay Marine on Merseyside.

Along with most other Scottish yards, Miller suffered from lack of orders. It built its final boat the 100ft steel trawler *Pursuit II* PD197 for Peterhead owners in 1992.

Postscript

In the early 1990s the outlook was bleak for many Scottish boatyards.

A report[7] published by the Sea Fish Industry Authority in 1993 pointed out a decline of 58 per cent in the number of Scottish yards building fishing vessels during the five years 1987 to 1992.

It expressed concern that the current rates of removing elderly boats and building new ones were not high enough to prevent the fleet from ageing. The review commented 'there is nothing to contradict the hypothesis that withdrawal of building grants and real reductions in the fleet earnings have been at least contributory factors in the decline in demand for new UK fishing vessel construction'.

Nevertheless, there was some cause for optimism at the start of 1994.

The Government had suspended the Days at Sea restrictions while the European Court decided whether or not the Act would be legal. Quotas for main North Sea stocks were slightly higher than in 1993 and the more powerful boats were showing an increasing interest in non-quota species such as grenadier, orange roughy and black scabbard in deepwater in the North Atlantic at the edge of the Continental Shelf.

Some skippers ordered new boats. Late in 1993 Macduff Shipyards delivered the 90ft steel trawler *Maranatha III* UL77 to Skippers Niven Ogg and Neil Rumbles. Designed to catch alternative species in deep water off west Scotland she had a colossal 17,000 gallon fuel capacity to enable her to work further afield if fishing opportunities arose elsewhere.

She was followed by the 76ft steel trawler *Atlas* BF182 for Skipper William West. Designed with deep water fisheries in mind she resembled *Westro* in many respects.

Early in 1994 a similar boat, larger than *Atlas* but smaller than *Maranatha III* was ordered from Macduff by Skipper Derek West. Jones Buckie Shipyard was building a 68ft steel trawler for Skipper Bruce Robertson. Designed by S. C. McAllister she had an exceptionally broad beam of 25ft.

By late 1994 Macduff had two or three more steel boats and two wooden hulled ones under construction or on order. Jones received an order for a 79ft steel trawler for Peterhead.

New designs.

Several yards and naval architects introduced new designs at the 'Fishing '94' exhibition in Aberdeen.

Campbeltown Shipyard showed plans of a steel 90 footer, with fuller deeper beamier hull form than the Campbeltown 87 class, and more powerful engine and deck machinery for deepwater work. Her engine could be 1,000hp and fuel capacity 17,560 gallons and her two trawl winches could each carry 3,000m of 24.2mm wire.

A new firm, Macduff Ship Design, had designed a hefty steel 90 footer with beam of almost 29ft and depth of 17ft. Her features included a bulbous stern which gives better water flow to the propeller.

Scottish fishermen are resourceful and resilient and are determined to see their industry survive.

[7]A review of UK Fishing Boat Building 1987/92.

APPENDIX

FISHING METHODS

One of the greatest influences on vessel design is the type of fishing gear being used. Boats are usually referred to by their means of fish capture as, for example 'trawler', 'purse seiner', or 'drifter'.

Constant reference to fishing methods is made throughout this book, so a very brief summary of the main types of fishing gear is included here as a general background to the vessel descriptions.

Single Boat Demersal Trawl.

This method is used to catch bottom-swimming or 'demersal' fish such as haddock, whiting, cod, saithe and plaice. A trawl consists of a funnel shaped net attached to the boat by two wire warps. As it is towed along the seabed the net mouth is kept open by floats and weights and otter doors.

Warp length is generally three-and-a-half to four times the water depth, and fish are caught in the cod end or 'bag'.

Trawls can be towed from the side of the boat or from the stern.

Pair-Trawl, or Midwater Trawl.

The pair trawl is used to fish at intermediate depths between the surface and seabed and is towed by two boats positioned some distance apart. The depth of the net is controlled primarily by warp length and the distance between the vessels.

It can be used to catch either demersal species or 'pelagic' fish such as herring, mackerel and sprats which swim in shoals in midwater or near the surface.

Flydragging Seine Net.

The seine net is used for catching demersal species on or close to the seabed.

It is basically similar to a small trawl with conical bag and long wings and is rigged with floats and weights.

Long warps are attached to the net and traditionally consist of coils of rope joined end to end.

A flag buoy or 'dhan' attached to the free end of the first rope is dropped overboard and the boat steams along paying out rope, and then the net is set. The second rope is payed out as the boat completes a triangular course back to the dahn where the end of the first rope is picked up.

While the boat moves ahead she hauls in the ropes simultaneously so that they gradually converge and herd the fish into the path of the net.

When the ropes are nearly closed and the net has overtaken and caught the fish the ropes are hauled quickly until the net is near the boat and ready for hauling aboard.

Purse Seine.

The purse seine catches pelagic fish such as herring, mackerel and sprats which congregate in dense shoals near the surface. Purse seining basically involves setting a huge net in a circle to form a wall of netting around the shoal. The net is rigged with floats and weights, and at its lower edge is a pursing wire running from the boat and through rings attached to the net by short ropes, and back to the boat.

When the pursing wire is hauled in by the winch the bottom of the net is drawn together or 'pursed', leaving the net lying like an enormous bowl containing the fish. The netting is hauled by means of a power block or net winch, forcing the shoal into a diminishing area of net until the fish are sufficiently dried up to be brailed or pumped into the boat.

Ring Net.

This is broadly similar to a small purse seine but is worked by two boats. It was used in shallow water near the coast and in sea lochs but went out of favour following the introduction of purse seining and pair trawling.

Drift Nets.

At one time the drift net was the chief method of catching herring. Sheets of netting were joined end to end in fleets of up to a hundred per boat. They hung in the water like a curtain, kept vertical by floats and buoys at the top and by a weighted sole rope.

After setting the gear the drifter lay moored to the nets by a messenger rope. Herring were caught in the mesh by their gills.

Great Lines.

These were lengths of thin rope with baited hooks attached at intervals by branch lines or snoods. A typical line measured three hundred fathoms and as many as forty or so were joined end to end and laid along or just off the seabed with an anchor and dahn at each end.

They were used by larger boats making trips of some three weeks to rocky ground mainly around the Faroes and Iceland and Rockall, and caught chiefly halibut, cod, ling, skate and tusk.

Small Lines.

Small lines are a lighter version of great lines and are worked by inshore vessels which return to port each day.

Scallop Dredges.

A typical scallop dredge consists of a triangular steel frame fitted with a toothed bar arranged at an angle to rake scallops off the seabed and into a bag attached to the frame and made of linked steel rings and heavy netting.

Dredges are towed along the seabed for a while before hauling.

BIBLIOGRAPHY

Arranged alphabetically by name of author

Peter F. Anson, *Fishing Boats and Fisher Folk on the East Coast of Scotland*. 1930 (Re-issued 1971).

Peter Brady, *Fishing Vessels of Britain and Ireland*. 1994 edition.

Gavin Cargill, *Blockade '75*. 1976.

John Dyson, *Business in Great Waters*. 1977.

Bill Macdonald, *Boats and Builders*. 1993.

Edgar J. March, *Sailing Drifters*. 1952. (Re-issued 1969).

Angus Martin, *The Ring Net Fishermen*.

Barry Milton, *Fishing Boat*. 1980.

Alexander Noble, *The Scottish Inshore Fishing Vessel Design, Construction and Repair*. 1978.

George F. Ritchie, *Real Price of Fish*. 1991.

Peter Smith, *The Lammas Drave and the Winter Herrin*. 1985.

Iain Sutherland, *From Herring to Seine Net Fishing on the East Coast of Scotland*.

David Thomson, *Seine Fishing*. 1981.

David Thomson, *Pair Trawling and Pair Seining*.

Gloria Wilson, *Scottish Fishing Craft*. 1965.

Gloria Wilson, *More Scottish Fishing Craft*. 1968.

Reports and Periodicals, various years.

Fishing News.

Commercial Fishing.

Classic Boat.

Scottish Fishing Weekly.

World Fishing.

Department of Agriculture and Fisheries for Scotland, Fisheries of Scotland Reports, and Scottish Sea Fisheries Statistical Tables.

Sea Fish Industry Authority (Formerly White Fish Authority) Annual Report and Accounts.